# MY LIFE

## A Collection of Memories

BARNES
& NOBLE
BOOKS

NEW YORK

Text design by Lundquist Design, New York

ISBN: 0-7607-5728-3

Printed and bound in the United States of America.

04 05 06 MC 6 5 4 3 2

# Table of Contents

# Ready to reminisce

The book you have in your hands may be the most important one you've ever read – but first, you have to write it. No one can tell your life story quite like you can, and there's no time like the present to understand your past and consider your future. People forget, photos fade, mementos break; the dustbin of history is full to overflowing with lost memories. But your life story is not to be discarded – it's your gift to your family, your gift to history, and most of all, your gift to yourself.

## How to use this book

Within this book you'll find room to accommodate even the most complex life story, with hundreds of pages to cover the entire span of your personal history from babyhood and family background through the prime of life and grandparenthood. Each chapter prompts memories and inspiration in five different ways:

## Questions

In this book are over a thousand questions – and that means you have a thousand possible places to begin telling your story. You don't have to write it in chronological order, either; try starting with the questions that come most easily to you. Just be sure you get around to the more sensitive topics eventually, because topics are only sensitive when they have deep personal meaning for you. Think of your story as a Renaissance painting: Only by exploring these shadowy areas that you've pushed to the background will you be able to find true perspective on your life. It doesn't matter where you begin to fill in the canvas, as long as you end with that fearless flourish.

## Quotes

In this book, your words will be right alongside those of literary greats, to inspire you to be just as bold as they were in answering life's questions. Don't worry so much about whether history will ultimately prove your answers right or wrong. The textbook version of history may be more thorough than yours, but it leaves a lot of room for personal interpretation. And when it comes to telling your life story, accuracy is secondary to honesty.

## Instant Memories

As you write, you'll notice that certain chapters of your life are left unresolved, and key players in your life story occasionally disappear for no apparent reason. You may find this dispiriting or distressing at first, but consider this: Your life story isn't over, and lost friends and mentors may yet be found. To reach closure and renew acquaintances, you don't have to force yourself to attend a high school reunion, either – just follow the suggestions outlined in the *Instant Memories* sections throughout the book. These sections add a spirit of adventure to your story too, daring you to journey to the land of your ancestors, or even venture a peek under your bed where all those shoeboxes of family photos are awaiting your discovery.

## Making History

The *Making History* sections throughout this book give you a chance to tell history from your perspective, and consider how major world events may have looked from the point of view of your parents and ancestors. Looking back, you may find that you're less than satisfied with the course of historical events – but with the action steps outlined in these sections, you can always make course corrections towards a better future. You may not be able to rewrite history entirely, but you can always choose to change history as you write it.

## Focus On...

Your life story is not yours alone. Ancestors, loved ones, teachers, pesky schoolmates and difficult bosses: all had a role in the ensemble drama of your life. The *Focus On...* sections make sure these people receive due credit – the great-uncle whose circus stories inspired you to try the trapeze, the neighbor who performed heroic feats of friendship for over a decade, the mentor who gave you the first big break in your career. *Focus On...* will also help you identify people who can refresh your memory, and help fill in any obvious gaps in your story. So in the process of completing this book, you will be renewing your connections with your family, your ancestors, and your community.

## Now, without further ado...

Pull out the old family photo albums, dust off those scrapbooks, gather your family and friends: this is your time to reminisce.

# CHAPTER I

# Way Back When: Family Origins

*Life can only be understood backwards; but it must be lived forwards.*

— Soren Kierkegaard

## Making History: Your family tree

Mark your mark on history by completing the family chart. Don't worry about exact dates of birth and death or birthplaces – concentrate instead on telling personal details about each family member. Knowing that your great-grandmother was born on March 14, 1879 is helpful, but that data would seem pretty dry compared to a juicy tidbit of family lore about how she was born on a boat coming to America. Think about stories you have heard about your ancestors, and ask other people in your family to help you fill in family facts and legends. Maybe your great-great-aunt was a notorious pirate, or your great-great-grandfather died in an accident building the first cross-country railroad. These are the stories that will bring your family tree to life, and make it bloom with living color.

**Me**
Circumstances of birth:

**Siblings:**
Circumstances of birth:

1.

2.

3.

4.

5.

**Mother**
Circumstances of birth:

Occupation(s):

Preoccupations:

Defining life events:

1.

2.

3.

**Father**
Circumstances of birth:

Occupation(s):

Preoccupations:

Defining life events:

1.

2.

3.

*Mothers side of the family
continues on page 3*

*Fathers side of the family
continues on page 6*

## Mother's side of family
(continued from page 2)

**Aunts/Uncles (mom's side)**
Circumstances of birth:
Sibling 1:
Sibling 2:
Sibling 3:

Occupations:
Sibling 1:
Sibling 2:
Sibling 3:

Preoccupations:
Sibling 1:
Sibling 2:
Sibling 3:

Defining life events:
Sibling 1:

Sibling 2:

Sibling 3:

**Maternal Grandmother**
Circumstances of birth:

Occupation(s):

Preoccupations:

Defining life events:

1.

2.

3.

*Maternal Grandmother's side of the family
continues on page 4*

**Maternal Grandfather**
Circumstances of birth:

Occupation(s):

Preoccupations:

Defining life events:

1.

2.

3.

*Maternal Grandfather's side of the family
continues on page 5*

## Mother's side of family
Maternal Grandmother's side
(continued from page 3)

**Great Aunts/Uncles (maternal grandmother's side)**
Circumstances of birth:
Sibling 1:
Sibling 2:
Sibling 3:

Occupations:
Sibling 1:
Sibling 2:
Sibling 3:

Preoccupations:
Sibling 1:
Sibling 2:
Sibling 3:

Defining life events:
Sibling 1:

Sibling 2:

Sibling 3:

**Maternal Great-Grandmother #1**
Circumstances of birth:

Occupation(s):

Preoccupations:

Defining life events:

1.

2.

**Maternal Great-Grandfather #1**
Circumstances of birth:

Occupation(s):

Preoccupations:

Defining life events:

1.

2.

## Mother's side of family
Maternal Grandfather's side
(continued from page 3)

---

**Great-Aunts/Uncles (maternal grandfather's side)**
Circumstances of birth:
Sibling 1:
Sibling 2:
Sibling 3:

Occupations:
Sibling 1:
Sibling 2:
Sibling 3:

Preoccupations:
Sibling 1:
Sibling 2:
Sibling 3:

Defining life events:
Sibling 1:

Sibling 2:

Sibling 3:

---

**Maternal Great-Grandmother #2**
Circumstances of birth:

Occupation(s):

Preoccupations:

Defining life events:

1.

2.

---

**Maternal Great-Grandfather #2**
Circumstances of birth:

Occupation(s):

Preoccupations:

Defining life events:

1.

2.

## Father's side of family
(continued from page 2)

**Aunts/Uncles (dad's side)**
Circumstances of birth:
Sibling 1:
Sibling 2:
Sibling 3:

Occupations:
Sibling 1:
Sibling 2:
Sibling 3:

Preoccupations:
Sibling 1:
Sibling 2:
Sibling 3:

Defining life events:
Sibling 1:

Sibling 2:

Sibling 3:

**Paternal Grandmother**
Circumstances of birth:

Occupation(s):

Preoccupations:

Defining life events:

1.

2.

3.

**Paternal Grandfather**
Circumstances of birth:

Occupation(s):

Preoccupations:

Defining life events:

1.

2.

3.

*Paternal Grandmother's side of the family continues on page 7*

*Paternal Grandfather's side of the family continues on page 8*

## Father's side of family
Paternal Grandmother's side
(continued from page 6)

**Great Aunts/Uncles (paternal grandmother's side)**
Circumstances of birth:
Sibling 1:
Sibling 2:
Sibling 3:

Occupations:
Sibling 1:
Sibling 2:
Sibling 3:

Preoccupations:
Sibling 1:
Sibling 2:
Sibling 3:

Defining life events:
Sibling 1:

Sibling 2:

Sibling 3:

**Paternal Great-Grandmother #1**
Circumstances of birth:

Occupation(s):

Preoccupations:

Defining life events:

1.

2.

**Paternal Great-Grandfather #1**
Circumstances of birth:

Occupation(s):

Preoccupations:

Defining life events:

1.

2.

## Father's side of family
Paternal Grandfather's side
(continued from page 6)

**Great Aunts/Uncles (Paternal grandfather's side)**
Circumstances of birth:
Sibling 1:
Sibling 2:
Sibling 3:

Occupations:
Sibling 1:
Sibling 2:
Sibling 3:

Preoccupations:
Sibling 1:
Sibling 2:
Sibling 3:

Defining life events:
Sibling 1:

Sibling 2:

Sibling 3:

**Paternal Great-Grandmother #2**
Circumstances of birth:

Occupation(s):

Preoccupations:

Defining life events:

1.

2.

**Paternal Great-Grandfather #2**
Circumstances of birth:

Occupation(s):

Preoccupations:

Defining life events:

1.

2.

## What's in a name?

What are the origins of your family name? Can you trace it back to a particular part of the world, or a specific trade that your ancestors once practiced? Does your name mean something in another language?

_____

_____

_____

_____

_____

_____

_____

_____

_____

What do you know about the origins of your mother's and grandmothers' maiden names?

_____

_____

_____

_____

_____

_____

_____

_____

_____

_____

Do you know if your family name was ever changed? Why? Was it altered by authorities when your ancestors arrived in this country, a slave name assigned by the owner of a plantation, changed very deliberately to avoid ethnic prejudice, or a stage or pen name by an ancestor with artistic ambitions?

_____

_____

_____

_____

_____

_____

Do any of your ancestors have particularly unusual or inventive names, and do you know how those names were chosen?

_____

_____

_____

_____

_____

_____

_____

Have any first or middle names been carried down in your family for generations? What is the origin of this name?

_____

_____

_____

_____

_____

_____

_____

## Mom's side of the family

What do you know about your great-great grandparents on your mother's side? Are there stories to tell?

_____

_____

_____

_____

_____

_____

Did you ever get a chance to know your maternal grandmother? If so, what is your most vivid memory of her?

_____

_____

_____

_____

_____

_____

_____

Based on your own experiences and family stories about your maternal grandmother, what five words do you think best describe her? How would you describe her daily work, and her role in your family?

_____

_____

_____

_____

_____

What about your maternal grandfather? What would you say is your most vivid memory of him?

_____

_____

_____

_____

_____

_____

_____

_____

_____

Based on your own experiences and family stories about your maternal grandfather, what five words do you think best describe him? How would you describe his daily work, and his role in your family?

_____

_____

_____

_____

_____

_____

_____

_____

_____

_____

How did your maternal grandparents first meet? What do you know about their courtship and subsequent relationship?

_____

_____

_____

_____

_____

_____

_____

_____

_____

_____

Who raised your mother, and what do you know about how she was raised? Was she raised in a home where they cracked jokes around the dinner table, or expected the kids to practice piano for hours, or got up to milk the cows at dawn?

_____

_____

_____

_____

_____

_____

_____

_____

## Dad's side of the family

What do you know about your great-great grandparents on your father's side? Have you heard any stories?

_____

_____

_____

_____

_____

_____

_____

Did you ever get a chance to know your paternal grandmother? If so, what is your most vivid memory of her?

_____

_____

_____

_____

_____

_____

_____

Based on your own experiences and family stories about your paternal grandmother, what five words do you think best describe her? How would you describe her daily work, and her role in your family?

_____

_____

_____

_____

_____

_____

What about your paternal grandfather? What would you say is your most vivid memory of him?

_____

_____

_____

_____

_____

_____

_____

_____

_____

Based on your own experiences and family stories about your paternal grandfather, what five words do you think best describe him? How would your describe his daily work, and his role in your family?

_____

_____

_____

_____

_____

_____

_____

_____

_____

How did your paternal grandparents first meet? What do you know about their courtship and subsequent relationship?

_____

_____

_____

_____

_____

_____

_____

_____

_____

Who raised your father, and what do you know about how he was raised? Was he raised in a home where they never had to make their own beds, or prayed before every meal, or played five-hour games of Monopoly?

_____

_____

_____

_____

_____

_____

_____

_____

_____

*There is a land of the living
and a land of the dead,
and the bridge is love.*

— *Thornton Wilder*

## Distinguishing characteristics

Is there any particular physical trait that distinguishes people in your family – floppy ears, giant toes, irrepressibly curly hair?  Did you inherit this trait?

_____

_____

_____

_____

_____

_____

_____

_____

_____

Does your family joke about this family trait, or are they proud of it? How did you feel about it when you were growing up? What about now?

_____

_____

_____

_____

_____

_____

_____

_____

_____

What kind of a reputation did your family seem to have back in your grandparents' day? Were they known as being raucous, generous, stubbornly self-reliant, or for some other prominent characteristic? How do you think they earned this reputation?

_____

_____

_____

_____

_____

_____

_____

_____

_____

_____

Are there any personality traits you share in common with one or more of your ancestors? Perhaps a fiery temper, an indelible optimism, or a tendency to worry too much? Describe.

_____

_____

_____

_____

_____

_____

_____

_____

_____

_____

## Running in the family

Is there any particular ability that seems to run in your family, such as a good head for numbers, a devilish sense of humor, or a knack for melodious whistling? Describe.

_____

_____

_____

_____

_____

_____

_____

_____

_____

_____

Has anyone in your family ever been recognized for special talents in this area? How so?

_____

_____

_____

_____

_____

_____

_____

_____

_____

Do people in your family tend to go into a particular line of work, or pursue a particular hobby? Are you part of this tradition?

_____
_____
_____
_____
_____
_____
_____
_____
_____
_____
_____

Was there ever any pressure on your parents or you or your siblings to keep up the family tradition in a particular skill or profession, or competition among family members in this area?

_____
_____
_____
_____
_____
_____
_____
_____
_____
_____

*If you cannot get rid of
the family skeleton, you
may as well make it dance.*

— George Bernard Shaw

## Focus on: Family legends

Every family has its legends, stories told at bedtime from parent to child for generations. In these stories, ancestors always seem to be doing amazing feats – surviving shipwrecks, running away with the circus, negotiating international peace treaties. Which story about your ancestors is your favorite? Please write it, as best you can remember it, below. If you're hazy on the details, you might consult a sibling or a cousin who can help fill them in.

_____

_____

_____

_____

_____

_____

_____

_____

_____

_____

_____

_____

_____

_____

_____

_____

_____

_____

_____

_____

_____

_____

_____

_____

_____

## Family Legends, cont.

Why was this particular story your favorite? Who was the character you identified with most of all, and what was your favorite part of the story? Was there a moral to this story, and if so, did it stick with you? Who do you remember telling you this story? Do you remember what funny voices or dramatic flourishes the storyteller added to make this story even funnier, or spookier, or more adventurous? How much of this story do you think is factual, and how much is pure fiction? If this story is based on any actual events or facts, please describe them briefly here.

_____

_____

_____

_____

_____

_____

_____

_____

_____

_____

_____

_____

_____

_____

_____

_____

_____

_____

_____

_____

_____

_____

_____

## Like grandma always said...

Are there any particular sayings you remember your grandparents or relatives repeating often? What are these catchphrases, and when did they usually come up in conversation?

_____

_____

_____

_____

_____

_____

_____

_____

_____

_____

_____

Why do you think these sayings were so relevant to your family way back when? Which sayings still hold true for you today?

_____

_____

_____

_____

_____

_____

_____

_____

_____

_____

_____

Did your elders ever tell you a certain action would bring luck or misfortune, such as crossing your eyes underwater, throwing salt over your shoulder, or hanging a talisman from the rear-view mirror? Did you ever believe in this superstition yourself? Do you still?

_____

_____

_____

_____

_____

_____

_____

_____

_____

If you were to choose a family motto, what would it be and why?

_____

_____

_____

_____

_____

_____

_____

_____

_____

_____

## A matter of faith
What religion did your ancestors on both sides of your family practice?

_____

_____

_____

_____

_____

_____

_____

_____

_____

Would you say your grandparents on either side of your family were deeply religious, mostly secular, or somewhere in between? Can you give some example of how their religious beliefs (or lack thereof) manifested themselves?

_____

_____

_____

_____

_____

_____

_____

_____

_____

Did any of your ancestors convert to another religion? How did the rest of your family react at the time?

_____

_____

_____

_____

_____

_____

_____

_____

_____

_____

What religious customs of your ancestors do you practice to this day, and which ones do you choose not to observe? Why?

_____

_____

_____

_____

_____

_____

_____

_____

_____

_____

## As is our custom

Would you say that at the time they were growing up, your grandparents' families would have been considered fairly traditional, or a little unconventional? How so? Can you give some examples?

_____

_____

_____

_____

_____

_____

Did any of your ancestors have any personal habits that seem a little unusual in retrospect – a flair for outlandish attire, a habit of swimming in frozen lakes? Can you recall any family legends about this eccentric behavior?

_____

_____

_____

_____

_____

_____

In your grandparents' day, were the men and women in your family treated very differently from one another? How so? How does this compare with your family today?

_____

_____

_____

_____

_____

_____

Are there any bad habits that seem to run in your family, whether as minor as slurping your soup or as major as excessive drinking? How has this affected your family over the years?

_____

_____

_____

_____

_____

_____

_____

_____

_____

_____

Are there any unconscious habits you suspect you've inherited from your family – snorting when you laugh, rubbing your forehead while thinking, walking with your hands clasped behind your back? Who else in your family shares this trait?

_____

_____

_____

_____

_____

_____

_____

_____

_____

## Such a gem

Is there any family heirloom that is particularly prized in your family? Please describe the object. How old is it? Where does it come from, and how did your family come by it?

_____

_____

_____

_____

_____

_____

_____

_____

_____

_____

What does this object mean to you personally? Does it hold any symbolic meaning for you? Do you remember where you first saw it?

_____

_____

_____

_____

_____

_____

_____

_____

_____

_____

_____

What do you think this heirloom is worth? Is its value monetary or mostly sentimental? Describe.

_____

_____

_____

_____

_____

_____

_____

_____

_____

_____

How did your ancestors manage to hang on to this treasure all these years? Was your family ever at risk of losing it? Who saved it, and how?

_____

_____

_____

_____

_____

_____

_____

_____

_____

*I can only sign over everything,*
*the house, the dog,*
*the ladders, the jewels,*
*the soul, the family tree, the mailbox.*
*Then I can sleep.*
*Maybe.*

— Anne Sexton

## Location, location, location...

When people ask you where your family is originally from, which places do you usually name first? Can you pinpoint the location to a particular country, region, province, county, hometown, or even neighborhood?

_____

_____

_____

_____

_____

_____

_____

_____

_____

_____

Why do you think this place looms so large in your family's history? Does your family still have personal or cultural ties there? Describe.

_____

_____

_____

_____

_____

_____

_____

_____

_____

Based on family lore or your own visits there, how would you describe this place? Start with a list of five adjectives, then add any details you know or have heard about how your ancestors lived under those conditions.

_____

_____

_____

_____

_____

_____

_____

_____

_____

_____

_____

Have you ever visited this place? Did you feel at home there at all? Do you still know relatives there?

_____

_____

_____

_____

_____

_____

_____

_____

_____

_____

*There's a magical tie to the*
*land of our home which*
*the heart cannot break,*
*though the footsteps may roam.*

*— Eliza Cook*

## Instant memories: Your ancestral home

Find out more about the area where one of your parents or grandparents was born and raised by rummaging through family memorabilia in the attic, making a research trip to the library, visiting the location, or all of the above. Then write a couple of paragraphs in the space below describing what life was like there in your ancestors' time. How many people lived there? How did most people there make a living? Back when your ancestors lived there, were most locals thriving or struggling just to get by? How was your family treated in this community? What language(s) were spoken there? Was the town famous or infamous for any reason?

Take or find a photo of the town where one of your parents or grandparents was raised. Dig around in your attic, and see if you can find a shot of what the town looked like back in those days. If you have a picture of the home where your parent or grandparent lived, that's great too. Scan the photo(s) on a computer and print it out in color at your local copy shop (the staff there should be able to help with this), or simply make a color photocopy of the photo.

Paste your picture(s) in the space below, then write a caption that draws attention to a few telling details:

What did the houses, buildings and roads look like back then? Do they still look this way? Note any buildings that were landmarks in your parent's or grandparent's life: school, place of worship, the City Hall where your grandparents got hitched, etc.

Are there any businesses in the picture that you remember hearing stories about – the barber where your great-grandpa bought his mustache wax, the general store where your great-aunt got caught stealing candy, the shoe repair shop your grandmother ran after her husband died?

If you have a photo of the family home, note any telling details and stories you heard about the place. Did they ever lock their doors? Was there running water, or a well and an outhouse? Were the nearest neighbors a mile away, or right downstairs?

All that is gold does not glitter,
Not all those who wander are lost;
The old that is strong does not wither,
Deep roots are not reached by the frost.

— J. R. R. Tolkein

## Home away from home

Did your ancestors ever leave their native land to settle in another part of the world? If so, what were their reasons for leaving – were they fleeing war or another calamity, transported involuntarily, seeking a better life, pursuing an international romance?

_____

_____

_____

_____

_____

_____

_____

Where did they ultimately settle, and why? What do you know about their journey to their adopted home, and the cultural, economic and other adjustments they had to make?

_____

_____

_____

_____

_____

_____

_____

Do you know what happened to the family members that stayed behind in their native land? How did their lives differ from the lives of those who left?

_____

_____

_____

_____

_____

_____

_____

Looking through old letters, postcards, and scrapbooks, can you tell whether your ancestors spend much time away from home? Where did they go, and why? Did they seem to enjoy their time there, or were they homesick?

_____

_____

_____

_____

_____

_____

_____

_____

_____

_____

Did any ancestor of yours ever make a daring or life-changing journey? Was there ever a roving flamenco guitarist, an Underground Railroad guide, or an Arctic explorer in your family?

_____

_____

_____

_____

_____

_____

_____

_____

_____

*Life began in mystery, and it will end in mystery, but what a savage and beautiful country lies in between.*

— Diane Ackerman

# CHAPTER TWO

# Ready for the world: Babyhood

*A baby is an inestimable blessing and bother.*

*— Mark Twain*

## Meet the parents

Do you know how your biological parents met? What do you know about their courtship?

_____

_____

_____

_____

_____

_____

_____

_____

_____

How old was your mother when she became pregnant with you, and what was her life like? How did having you change her life?

_____

_____

_____

_____

_____

_____

_____

_____

_____

_____

What about your biological father? What was his life like when you came along, and how did your arrival change it?

_____

_____

_____

_____

_____

_____

_____

_____

_____

_____

When you were you were a baby and a toddler, who was your primary parent: one or both birth parents, step-parents, foster or adoptive parents, someone else? What's your earliest memory of this person? If you were adopted as a child, what do you remember about your adoption day?

_____

_____

_____

_____

_____

_____

_____

_____

_____

_____

## The big event

Where was your mother when she went into labor, and what was she doing there? How did she manage to get someplace where she could get medical assistance? Who was there to help?

_____

_____

_____

_____

_____

_____

_____

_____

_____

What do you know about the circumstances of your birth? Were you born prematurely or right on time, and were there any complications or tense moments?

_____

_____

_____

_____

_____

_____

_____

_____

_____

What were your immediate family members doing when you were born? Who were the first people to greet you when you were born?

_____

_____

_____

_____

_____

_____

_____

_____

_____

_____

Do you know how your birth or adoptive parents reacted when they saw you for the very first time? What about other family members?

_____

_____

_____

_____

_____

_____

_____

_____

_____

_____

*Dear Mary: We all knew you had it in you.*

*— Dorothy Parker, in a telegram to a friend who had given birth*

## Making history: The year you were born

Since we are all a product of the times we live in, you can learn a lot about yourself with a little historical research. Dig around online and at your local library to find out what was happening the year you were born, and you'll gain insight into what may have been on the minds of the people who were raising you. Do your best to cover these historical bases:

**Politics:** Who were the political leaders of the country at the time? Were there any watershed political events that year that worried people, or gave them hope? Were there any political issues that seemed to divide or unite people?

**Economics:** Was the economy in good or bad shape the year you were born? Was there popular strife over economic conditions in the country, or were many people enjoying a comfortable standard of living? What was the economic outlook like for people in your parents' age, cultural, and educational demographic and geographic location?

**Culture:** What were the dominant trends in popular culture the year you were born? Were there any innovations in music, literature, art, theater, dance, fashion or film that indicated there was a cultural shift or new subculture in the making? What kind of music, literature and fashion were popular among people in your parents' demographic? Were there any films, art or theater shows at that time that were inspiring young people, or stirring up controversy?

_____

_____

_____

_____

_____

_____

_____

_____

_____

_____

_____

_____

_____

Once you know what was happening historically, try to find out how this affected your parents personally through family interviews or rummaging through family memorabilia. Did economic or political events have them worried about your prospects in life? How were they able to provide for you? What did your parents think of the movies and books that came out that year? What kind of music did they identify with? Did their experiences run against the grain, or closely match the main cultural, economic and political trends? Did they particularly support or take a stand on any political or social issue of the day? Did their responses to unfolding events at that time ever cause any divisions within the extended family, or draw the family closer together? Describe.

_____

_____

_____

_____

_____

_____

_____

_____

_____

_____

_____

_____

_____

_____

_____

_____

_____

_____

_____

_____

_____

*History can suggest to us alternatives that we would never otherwise consider. It can both warn and inspire.*

— Howard Zinn

## Historic sites

What is the place of birth listed on your birth certificate or adoption papers? How would you describe the town and nation of your birth, based on family stories and any memories you may have of it?

_____

_____

_____

_____

_____

_____

_____

_____

_____

_____

Where did your mother give birth to you? Were you born in a hospital, at home, or elsewhere? Was modern medical equipment available, or were the conditions considerably more rustic? Describe.

_____

_____

_____

_____

_____

_____

_____

_____

_____

_____

When your birth or adoptive parents took you to your new home for the very first time, where did they take you? Based on family stories and any memories you may have, how would you describe that home?

_____

_____

_____

_____

_____

_____

_____

_____

_____

_____

_____

_____

_____

_____

_____

_____

_____

_____

_____

_____

_____

_____

*Home is the place where,*
*when you have to go there,*
*They have to take you in.*

— Robert Frost

## All in the family

When you came along, did your parents already have other kids? If so, what were their ages when you were born? Based on family stories and what you can remember, how did they interact with you when you were very little? If you don't have older siblings, do you wish you had? Why or why not?

_____

_____

_____

_____

_____

Did other siblings come along after you were born? If so, how old were you when they were born? Based on family stories and what you can remember, how did you react when they arrived on the scene? If you don't have younger siblings, do you wish you had? Why or why not?

_____

_____

_____

_____

_____

Do you think your personal interactions or behavior later in life reflects your birth order or only child status in some way? Describe.

_____

_____

_____

_____

_____

Besides your birth or adoptive parents, who is the first member of your family that you remember? What is your earliest memory of this person?

_____

_____

_____

_____

_____

_____

_____

_____

_____

_____

Based on family stories, what relatives seemed to have a special bond with you as a baby or toddler? Describe.

_____

_____

_____

_____

_____

_____

_____

_____

_____

_____

## Naming names

How did your parents choose your first name? Does this name have any special meaning in your family, or in another language?

_____

_____

_____

_____

_____

_____

_____

Do you know what other names your parents were considering for you, and why these names ultimately weren't selected?

_____

_____

_____

_____

_____

_____

_____

What about a middle name? Do you have one, or even more than one? What do you know about the origins of your middle name(s)?

_____

_____

_____

_____

_____

_____

_____

Do you think your name suits you? Why or why not?

_____

_____

_____

_____

_____

_____

_____

Did you ever change your first, middle, or last name, or think about changing it? To what? Why?

_____

_____

_____

_____

_____

_____

_____

_____

When you were very little, what pet names or nicknames did your family call you? Did any of these stick? Why or why not?

_____

_____

_____

_____

_____

_____

## Child prodigy

Did you ever learn to do something before people expected you to – crawl, walk, talk, sing, spell, count, dance? Does this feat give any indication of the talents you developed later on, or in any way reflect the person you grew into as an adult? Describe.

_____

_____

_____

_____

_____

_____

_____

_____

_____

_____

What kinds of pictures did you draw when you were very little? Describe. Looking at them now, what do you see in those pictures?

_____

_____

_____

_____

_____

_____

_____

_____

_____

Was there any feat you could perform as a toddler that gave your family special delight – making funny faces, reciting the alphabet backwards, inventing wild stories about spaceships? Can you still do this? Do you think this early positive reinforcement had any impact on the person you now are?

_____

_____

_____

_____

_____

_____

_____

_____

_____

_____

_____

_____

_____

_____

_____

_____

_____

_____

_____

_____

_____

_____

_____

*Lord, grant that I may*
*always desire more*
*than I can accomplish.*

*— Michelangelo di Buonarotti*

## Focus on: Firsts

Put your memory to the ultimate test, and see how far back you can remember. What is the very first thing you can recall – your mom singing you a nursery rhyme, watching a mobile spin on the ceiling, your older brother chasing you around the living room? How old were you when this took place? Are there any other memories from when you were very little that stand out in your mind? What is your first happy memory? What about your first troubling or sad one? Capture a few of these in the space below. Try to remember these events from your own perspective, instead of just what you've been told about them.

_____

_____

_____

_____

_____

_____

_____

_____

_____

_____

_____

_____

_____

_____

_____

_____

_____

_____

_____

_____

Now consult a few relatives and others who knew you to help fill in a few more details about your early years, and provide another perspective. What was your first word, besides "mama" or "papa"? How do you think you picked up this word? Who is the very first friend you made outside your family? How did you become so attached to this person? What additional formative events can others recall taking place in your early years? What is the first event that seemed to make you especially happy or sad? How different are their memories of you from your own, and what light do these differences shed on your relationship then and now?

_____

_____

_____

_____

_____

_____

_____

_____

_____

_____

_____

_____

_____

_____

_____

_____

_____

_____

_____

## Quite a looker

When you were born, what did you look like – did you have hair, were you chubby, were you born with any birthmarks or other distinguishing physical traits? Do you still look the same in any way as you did when you were born?

_____

_____

_____

_____

_____

_____

_____

_____

_____

_____

Given photos you've seen and what you've been told, did you have a strong family resemblance to others in your biological family? Were there any physical features that especially made you look like your relatives, or distinguished you from the rest of your family?

_____

_____

_____

_____

_____

_____

_____

_____

When you were very little, did people say you looked a lot like a particular person in your family? Who? Do you think it was true? If so, did you have anything else in common, or any special kinship? Do you still look like this person?

_____

_____

_____

_____

_____

_____

_____

_____

_____

_____

Can you describe how you looked as a toddler? Did you continue to look much like this for years, or have your looks changed a great deal over time? How so?

_____

_____

_____

_____

_____

_____

_____

_____

_____

_____

## Baby talk

As a child, did you learn to speak in a language other than English, or in more than one language? Can you still speak in this other language, if only a few words? Why or why not?

_____

_____

_____

_____

_____

_____

_____

_____

_____

_____

Were there any words you couldn't really pronounce as a toddler? How did you pronounce these words instead?

_____

_____

_____

_____

_____

_____

_____

_____

_____

Did you have your own made-up words for anything when you were very little? Describe.

_____

_____

_____

_____

_____

_____

_____

_____

_____

_____

Is there anything you said as a baby that struck your family as especially funny or wise? Do tell.

_____

_____

_____

_____

_____

_____

_____

_____

_____

*A good laugh is sunshine in a house.*

— William Makepeace Thackeray

## Little angel, little devil

Are there any stories about you getting into trouble when you were very little, or giving your parents a terrible scare? Do tell.

_____

_____

_____

_____

_____

_____

_____

_____

Is there something you did as a baby or toddler that your family found especially endearing? Describe.

_____

_____

_____

_____

_____

_____

_____

_____

When you threw temper tantrums as a toddler, what kind of reaction did you usually get? Did your family bribe you, punish you, or let you cry yourself out? Can you recall an example of this?

_____

_____

_____

_____

_____

_____

_____

_____

_____

_____

Were you usually a happy baby, or did you cry a lot? What did it usually take to quiet you down?

_____

_____

_____

_____

_____

_____

_____

_____

_____

*Man is born to trouble,*
*as the sparks fly upward.*

*— The Book of Job*

## Instant memories: Then & now

Early childhood development can have a great impact on the adults we become. Consider how your early experiences shaped your life in the following ways, and jot down your responses in the space below.

**Inspiration:** What captured your imagination most when you were very young? Was there a particular story, game, picture or activity that completely captivated your interest? Does this relate to your interests as an adult, and if so, how?

**Talents:** What abilities seemed to come to you most naturally as a child? Does this relate to any talents you developed later on in life, or your choice of career or hobbies?

**Challenges:** What activities seem to be the most difficult for you early on? Did you find a way to overcome these difficulties, or figure out a way to work around or compensate for them? Do any of these early difficulties relate to challenges you experienced later on in life?

**Fear:** What did you seem to be most afraid of as a child? Does this still give you the creeps? If not, can you recall how and when you overcome that fear?

**Comfort:** What brought you the greatest comfort as a very young child?

_____

_____

_____

_____

_____

_____

_____

_____

_____

_____

_____

_____

_____

_____

_____

_____

Now that you are grown, you can put your early years into perspective.

**Parenting:** Can you think of any instances where the people who raised you proved to be especially wise or brave in their parenting decisions? What about a time when you think they could have been more thoughtful or responsible?

**Appreciation:** Is there anyone you wish you had a chance to thank for the love and thoughtfulness they showed towards you early on? Try writing a few words of thanks to this person in the space below.

**Regrets:** Is there any event that occurred in your very early life that you wish you could undo?

**Character development:** Is there a story about you as a baby that your family loved to tell about you or tease you about? Do tell. Did this story ever embarrass you because it reveals something about you that you didn't want others to know? Have you changed this aspect of your character, or come to terms with it?

_____

_____

_____

_____

_____

_____

_____

_____

_____

_____

_____

_____

_____

_____

_____

_____

_____

## Early favorites

What was your favorite toy as a baby? Did you give it a name? Do you know what became of it?

_____

_____

_____

_____

_____

_____

_____

_____

_____

_____

According to your family, was there a particular song that always seemed to quiet you down, that you loved singing, or that you demanded to hear over and over again? Can you still hum the tune, or remember the lyrics? Do you still enjoy this kind of music?

_____

_____

_____

_____

_____

_____

_____

_____

_____

_____

Was there a certain kind of food you just couldn't get enough of as a toddler? Do you still crave this as comfort food?

_____

_____

_____

_____

_____

_____

_____

_____

_____

_____

_____

What was your favorite bedtime story as a toddler? Looking back, does it surprise you that you were so fascinated by this story, or does it make perfect sense? Why?

_____

_____

_____

_____

_____

_____

_____

_____

_____

_____

_____

*Each time a new baby is born there is a possibility of reprieve. Each child is a new being, a potential prophet, a new spiritual prince, a new spark of light precipitated into the outer darkness.*

— R.D. Laing

# CHAPTER THREE

# Kidding around: Childhood

*Adorable children are considered
to be the general property of
the human race. Rude children
belong to their mothers.*

*— Judith Martin, a.k.a. Miss Manners*

## Fun and games

What did you enjoy doing most as a kid – drawing pictures, collecting rocks, playing cops and robbers? Do you still enjoy some variation of this activity? Explain.

_____

_____

_____

_____

_____

_____

_____

_____

_____

Please list some of your favorite movies, music, and books as a kid. What do you think impressed you so much about each of these back then?

_____

_____

_____

_____

_____

_____

_____

_____

_____

_____

What types of special outings did you like best: going to the park, movies, museum, or zoo? Did you get to do this kind of thing very often? Can you describe one such outing that you can remember?

_____

_____

_____

_____

_____

_____

_____

_____

_____

_____

_____

What did you usually do during recess at school? Did you ever get in trouble for your playground escapades, or get someone else in trouble? Describe.

_____

_____

_____

_____

_____

_____

_____

_____

_____

_____

_____

## Focus on: Imagination

What were your favorite creative outlets as a child – pictures, school plays, choir, stories, music, poems, crafts projects, dancing, comics, costumes? What are your best memories of this as a child? Were you ever nervous about expressing yourself? Why or why not? What would you say is your best example of creative expression from when you were a kid? What does this say about the child you were then? What about the person you are now?

_____

_____

_____

_____

_____

_____

_____

_____

_____

_____

_____

_____

_____

_____

_____

_____

_____

_____

_____

_____

_____

_____

_____

## Focus on: Imagination, cont.

Were you ever told by adults that you had an overactive imagination? Why do you think this was said about you – and do you think it was ever true? Did you ever invent any imaginary friends or foes, such as monsters under the bed? Describe. How much of a workout does your imagination get these days? Has your imagination served you well or gotten you into trouble as an adult? Explain.

_____

_____

_____

_____

_____

_____

_____

_____

_____

_____

_____

_____

_____

_____

_____

_____

_____

_____

_____

_____

_____

_____

When I was a child, adults would tell me not to make things up, warning me of what would happen if I did. As far as I can tell so far it seems to involve lots of foreign travel and not having to get up too early in the morning.

— Neil Gaiman

## Off to school

Do you have any strong memories from kindergarten – your first day, your teacher, the other kids? Describe.

_____

_____

_____

_____

_____

_____

Who was your favorite teacher in elementary school? What about your least favorite? What did these teachers have to say about you on your report card or in parent-teacher conferences?

_____

_____

_____

_____

_____

_____

_____

What were your favorite and least favorite subjects in elementary school? What made those subjects so fun or frustrating for you?

_____

_____

_____

_____

_____

_____

Was there a school project you especially enjoyed doing – a school play, a historical diorama, a spelling bee? Explain. What about a school project you intensely disliked?

_____

_____

_____

_____

_____

_____

_____

How did you get to and from school, and how long did it take? Can you remember any times you had difficulty getting to or from school – missing the bus, getting snowed in, being waylaid by bullies? Describe.

_____

_____

_____

_____

_____

_____

_____

Describe your elementary school: where it was, how it looked, and the kind of education they provided there. Were there any rules or teaching philosophies that strike you now as especially wise, or entirely wrong? Do you think you got a good education there overall, or was there something the school was sorely lacking?

_____

_____

_____

_____

_____

... We hear the teachers
as if they were far off, speaking
down a tube. Sometimes
a whole sentence gets through.
But the teachers don't give up.
They rise, dress, appear before us
Crisp and hopeful. They have a plan.

— Naomi Shihab Nye

**Among friends**

Were you ever particularly close to any sibling or relative as a kid? Who was it, and why do you think you were so close? Can you recall an adventure you had together?

_____

_____

_____

_____

_____

_____

_____

_____

_____

_____

Did you ever have a best friend as a kid? Who was it, and how did you become such fast friends? What is your fondest memory of this person?

_____

_____

_____

_____

_____

_____

_____

_____

_____

_____

Can you remember ever having a crush on a classmate in elementary school? Who was the object of your affections, and what made this kid so special? How did you express your feelings – a homemade Valentine, merciless teasing, saving the seat next to you on the bus? What was the response?

_____

_____

_____

_____

_____

_____

_____

_____

_____

_____

Was there ever a time when someone befriended you or came to your rescue – when you'd gotten stuck on a math problem, lost your lunch money, or became an easy target in a game of dodge ball? Describe. What would you like to say to this kind person today, if you could?

_____

_____

_____

_____

_____

_____

_____

_____

_____

*There are some things you*
*can't share without ending up liking*
*each other, and knocking out*
*a twelve-foot mountain troll*
*is one of them.*

— J.K. Rowling

## Authority figures

As a kid, which authority figures did you fear most and why – your Girl Scout leader, your gym teacher, the boss on your paper route? Who did you think was the most reasonable, and why?

_____

_____

_____

_____

_____

_____

Who usually took care of you when a parent or guardian couldn't: a childcare professional, an adult relative or friend of the family, or an older kid or sibling who got paid to look after you? How did you feel about this arrangement at the time? Looking back, do you think you were easy to look after, or a bit of a terror?

_____

_____

_____

_____

_____

_____

Who was your favorite babysitter, and why? Were there any babysitters you particularly dreaded? If so, why?

_____

_____

_____

_____

_____

When you behaved badly, how did your parents react – a scolding, a time-out, a guilt trip, a strong backhand? What effect did this have on your behavior at the time? What effect do you think it's had long-term?

_____

_____

_____

_____

_____

_____

_____

_____

_____

_____

When you were told you weren't allowed to do something, how did you usually respond? Can you give an example? How do you react today when you're told what you can and can't do?

_____

_____

_____

_____

_____

_____

_____

_____

_____

*Children have never been very good at listening to their elders, but they have never failed to imitate them.*

— James Baldwin

## School's out

What did your family usually do on weekends? What was your favorite thing to do on weekends?

_____

_____

_____

_____

_____

_____

What did you usually do in the summertime back then? What summer stands out as the most memorable in your childhood? Describe.

_____

_____

_____

_____

_____

_____

Did you ever go to camp? If so, what is your best memory from camp? What about the worst?

_____

_____

_____

_____

_____

_____

Which holiday was always your favorite as a kid, and why? How did you usually prepare yourself for that holiday? On the night before the holiday, was it hard for you to get to sleep?

_____

_____

_____

_____

_____

_____

_____

What is the best present you ever received as a child? What about the worst?

_____

_____

_____

_____

_____

_____

_____

What was your favorite family vacation back then, and why? What about your least favorite?

_____

_____

_____

_____

_____

_____

_____

## Taking an interest

When you were a kid, did you ever participate in after-school activities – a youth group, saxophone lessons, gymnastics? If so, can you remember any stories from the time you spent in these activities?

_____

_____

_____

_____

_____

_____

_____

_____

_____

_____

When you were little, what did you want to be when you grew up? Have you actually pursued this line of work, or have your career ambitions changed since then? Explain.

_____

_____

_____

_____

_____

_____

_____

_____

_____

In pursuing your interests, did you ever win any awards or special achievements? Which are you most proud of, and why?

_____

_____

_____

_____

_____

_____

_____

_____

_____

_____

Were there certain interests you wanted to pursue as a kid that proved difficult for you – possibly because lessons cost too much, or your parents disapproved, or it required physical ability you lacked? How did you handle this limitation, or work around it?

_____

_____

_____

_____

_____

_____

_____

_____

_____

_____

*Don't let that horse*
*eat that violin*
*cried Chagall's mother*
*But he*
*kept right on*
*painting*

— *Lawrence Ferlinghetti*

## Instant memories: Daydream believer

Do one thing you always wanted to do as a child, but never had the chance – ride in a hot air balloon, tell off a bully, send a thank-you note to your third-grade reading teacher. Afterwards, capture the experience in writing below.

## Instant memories: Daydream believer, cont.

Now that you're back in touch with your childhood sense of wonder, don't stop there. Keep dreaming with any of these techniques:

**Double-dare yourself.** Challenge yourself by trying something you never thought you were any good at as a child. Go ahead – play a game of kickball, make a mug out of clay, tell a joke in public. How did it go? Describe below.

**Go with a whim.** As a kid, was there a place you wanted to visit, a toy you desperately wanted to play with, or a movie you weren't allowed to see? Treat yourself, then write about the experience below.

**Pass it on.** What advantages did you lack in your own childhood that you are now in a position to provide – help with math homework, a place to go after school, an adult's undivided attention a couple of hours a week? Give kids a chance to realize their dreams by making a donation or volunteering at a local school, after-school program, or family services program. Then write about it below.

_____

_____

_____

_____

_____

_____

_____

_____

_____

_____

_____

_____

_____

_____

_____

_____

_____

*Those who dream by day are cognizant of many things that escape those who dream only at night.*

— Edgar Allan Poe

## No place like home

What home do you most associate with your childhood, and who lived there with you? Who was at home with you most often? Did you share a room? If so, who shared it with you, and how did you get along in those close quarters?

_____

_____

_____

_____

_____

_____

_____

_____

_____

Describe personal landmarks in the neighborhood where you grew up: places you played, yards you mowed, treehouses where boys were strictly banned. What local places did you like best, and which did you like least? Why?

_____

_____

_____

_____

_____

_____

_____

_____

_____

_____

Where did you remember feeling most at home as a child – in your living room, at a neighbor's, in the woods, at the library, or some other special place? Explain.

_____

_____

_____

_____

_____

_____

_____

_____

_____

_____

Describe any pets you looked forward to seeing when you got home from school – name, species, temperament, and any distinguishing characteristics. What do you recall about how each of your pets lived and died? What's your favorite story about a pet?

_____

_____

_____

_____

_____

_____

_____

_____

_____

_____

**Family life**

What were the ground rules for family behavior in your house? Did you ever break any of these? Describe. What were the consequences?

_____

_____

_____

_____

_____

_____

_____

Can you think of one advantage you had over other kids you knew at the time – economic, educational, or otherwise? What about a disadvantage?

_____

_____

_____

_____

_____

_____

_____

Can you remember any particularly happy event in your family? Describe. How did you feel about it then? When you think about it now, how does it make you feel?

_____

_____

_____

_____

_____

_____

_____

Did your family go through any major upheaval when you were a child – divorce, economic crisis, estrangement from relatives, trouble with the law? How did this affect you at the time? Do you think it still affects you? Please explain.

_____

_____

_____

_____

_____

_____

_____

Was there any religious practice or ritual your family observed on a daily basis? What about on a weekly basis, or on holidays? How do you remember feeling about this practice at the time? How do you feel about it now?

_____

_____

_____

_____

_____

_____

_____

What was a typical daily menu at your house? Who cooked, and how good were they at it? Which foods were your favorites, and which did you put up a fuss about having to eat? How did your parents react?

_____

_____

_____

_____

_____

*Madam, there's no such thing*
*as a tough child — if you parboil*
*them first for seven hours,*
*they always come out tender.*

*— W.C. Fields*

## Defining moments

Did you ever experience any tragedies or serious illness as a child? How did you cope with it at the time? What do you think you learned from this experience about dealing with setbacks in life?

_____

_____

_____

_____

_____

_____

_____

_____

_____

Did your family ever move when you were a kid, or did you change schools? What were those first days in a new neighborhood or at a new school like for you? What kind of adjustments did you have to make, and who helped you make the transition?

_____

_____

_____

_____

_____

_____

_____

_____

_____

Were you ever bullied or mocked by another kid? If so, what excuses did the bully give for picking on you, and how did you handle it? Did you ever bully or mock another kid? If so, how and why?

_____

_____

_____

_____

_____

_____

_____

_____

_____

What would you say was your proudest moment as a child? What about your least proud moment?

_____

_____

_____

_____

_____

_____

_____

_____

_____

_____

*I was a very ancient twelve;
my views at that age would have
done credit to a Civil War veteran.
I am much younger now than
I was at twelve — or anyway,
less burdened.*

— Flannery O'Conner

## Making history: Making headlines

Do a little research to jog your memory, and note below ten pivotal historical events that occurred when you were a kid. What important laws were passed, what wars began and ended, what art or music shook up the world? Next to each of these historical events, note how this affected you and your family. Did it give you nightmares, anxieties, new hopes or higher expectations?

_____

_____

_____

_____

_____

_____

_____

_____

_____

_____

_____

_____

_____

_____

_____

_____

_____

_____

_____

_____

_____

Now take a look at today's headlines. How would you say the world has changed for the better since you were a kid? How has it changed for the worse? Explain. Then write three headlines that you'd like to see appear in the newspaper announcing events that make the world a better place to be a kid.

_____

_____

_____

_____

_____

_____

_____

_____

_____

_____

_____

_____

_____

_____

_____

_____

_____

_____

_____

_____

_____

When we talk about leaving our childhood behind us, we might as well say that the river flowing onward to the sea had left the fountain behind.

— Anna Jameson

# CHAPTER FOUR

# Teen dreams: Adolescence

*How true Daddy's words when he said: "All children must look after their own upbringing. Parents can only give good advice or put them on the right paths, but the final forming of a person's character lies in their own hands."*

*— Anne Frank*

## Taking on responsibilities

What responsibilities did you have around the house as a teen: making dinner twice a week, taking out the trash, preventing your room from being declared an environmental disaster? Which of these chores was no problem, and which did you put off for as long as possible? Why?

_____

_____

_____

_____

_____

_____

_____

_____

_____

Did you ever have a paying job as a teenager? How did you land this job? Describe a typical day on the job – your tasks, the working conditions, your boss, the uniform, your hours. Were you proud of your job, or was it a drag? When did you leave this job, and why?

_____

_____

_____

_____

_____

_____

_____

_____

What's the first major purchase you bought with your own money: your first car, a leather jacket, the complete works of Shakespeare? How long did you have to save up for this? Was it worth it?

_____

_____

_____

_____

_____

_____

_____

Did you ever have any adventures in babysitting – or misadventures, as the case may be? Describe.

_____

_____

_____

_____

_____

_____

_____

Did your family ever host a foreign exchange student that you were supposed to help and keep company? If so, what stories about the experience stand out in your mind?

_____

_____

_____

_____

_____

_____

_____

*Few things help an individual more than to place responsibility upon him, and to let him know that you trust him.*

— Booker T. Washington

## Your crowd

Who were your closest friends in junior high and high school? How would you describe each of them? What did you usually do together?

_____

_____

_____

_____

_____

_____

_____

Can you remember any of the slang kids used back then? Define a few of these expressions. Do you still catch yourself saying any of these things today?

_____

_____

_____

_____

_____

_____

_____

Can you think of a time when you decided to not go along with the crowd as a teenager, even though you knew it might raise some eyebrows?

_____

_____

_____

_____

_____

_____

How would you characterize the different cliques or social groups in your junior high and high school? Which ones did you hang out with most often, and which ones did you have problems with? Why?

_____

_____

_____

_____

_____

_____

_____

Can you recall ever making a special effort to fit in or stand out – wearing a particular style of clothes, smoking in the parking lot, dating a popular kid who was actually kind of boring? Describe. Did you succeed in your efforts? How did you feel about yourself afterwards?

_____

_____

_____

_____

_____

_____

_____

Did you spend much time and energy trying to be popular in your teen years? Why or why not? Do you invest more or less time impressing people these days? Explain.

_____

_____

_____

_____

_____

_____

*Avoid popularity if you would have peace.*

— Abraham Lincoln

## Instant Memories: Reunited

List three people who were important to you as a teenager in each of the categories below, and why they were so important.

_____

_____

_____

_____

**Best buddies:** Friends who helped you study for the final exam, who you trusted to give you a home perm, whose shoulders you cried on when your perm went horribly wrong, etc.

_____

_____

_____

**Accomplices:** The friend you passed notes with during health class, the other girl who played the drums in band, the cousin who helped you fix up your car and gave you a lift when it broke down, etc.

_____

_____

_____

**Mentors:** Your track coach, the English teacher who encouraged you to apply for college, the boss who started your culinary career by promoting you from busboy to short order cook, etc.

_____

_____

_____

**Teammates:** Fellow members of the swim team, chess club, student council, etc.

_____

_____

_____

## [Instant Memories: Reunited, cont.

Now look over your list. Which of these people have you lost touch with since high school? What would you like to say to them if you could? Jot down a few words below. Then track down one of these people, and tell them what you have to say in a letter, on the phone, or in person (if possible). Then write about it here afterwards. How did it feel? Was the response what you anticipated? Did this give you a sense of closure, or it did give you a chance to pick up where you left off with this person? Do tell.

_____

_____

_____

_____

_____

_____

_____

_____

_____

_____

_____

_____

_____

_____

_____

_____

_____

_____

_____

_____

_____

_____

_____

*I am indebted to my father for living,*
*but to my teacher for living well.*

— Alexander the Great

## Looking sharp

How did you usually dress as a teen? What was your favorite outfit? Did you sport certain signature fashions worn by kids who ran in your crowd, or did your fashion sense stand out in some way? Describe.

_____

_____

_____

_____

_____

_____

_____

What was the best you think you looked as a teen? What about the worst? Describe your look on both occasions – the ensemble you wore, the height of your hair, shoes so pointy your toes went numb, etc.

_____

_____

_____

_____

_____

_____

What kind of hairdo did you have, and how long did it take you to get it looking just right? To get it to look that way, did you require any special equipment, frequent trips to the hairdresser, or industrial-strength products? Explain.

_____

_____

_____

_____

_____

_____

Did you wear makeup back then? If so, how long did your typical makeup application take? What colors did you use? Did you wear it just when you felt like it, or would you not dream of leaving home without it? If so, why do you think makeup was so important to you – to blend in with other kids at school, to mask features you didn't think were attractive, or to win the admiration of your peers as being fashion-forward? How did your parents feel about your makeup?

_____

_____

_____

_____

_____

_____

_____

_____

What did you look like in your senior picture? Describe your pose, your outfit, your hairstyle. What is your immediate reaction to this picture today: "Looking sharp!" or "Wish I still had those cat-eye glasses…" or perhaps "What was I thinking with such gigantic lapels?!"

_____

_____

_____

_____

_____

_____

_____

_____

## School spirit

Were you proud of your high school? Why or why not? What about now?

_____

_____

_____

_____

_____

_____

_____

_____

_____

_____

Did your school have any rivals that stand out in your mind? What was the source of the rivalry – basketball championships, debate club contests, competing productions of _The Sound of Music?_ Did kids from your school ever play any pranks on the rival school, or vice versa? Did you participate?

_____

_____

_____

_____

_____

_____

_____

_____

_____

_____

Did you ever try out for cheerleading, the marching band, or the drum major squad? If so, what was that try-out like for you? If you made the cut, what can you remember about your first half-time show? If you never tried out for these school activities, what did you think about people who did?

_____

_____

_____

_____

_____

_____

_____

_____

_____

_____

Did you ever run for student council? Why or why not? If so, what was your campaign slogan, who were you running against, and how did it turn out? If you were elected, please describe a highlight of your career in student government. If you weren't elected, did you ever regret running? Why or why not?

_____

_____

_____

_____

_____

_____

_____

_____

_____

_____

_____

## Making the grade

How were your grades in junior high and high school? What's the worst grade you ever got on a test? Why do you think you did so poorly on this one? What about your best grade? What inspired you to do so well? Can you remember your teacher's comments in either case?

_____

_____

_____

_____

_____

_____

_____

_____

_____

Were grades important to you? Why or why not? Were you ever accused of being a slacker, or a grade-grubber? Do you think this was a fair accusation at the time or not? How is your approach to learning similar or different today?

_____

_____

_____

_____

_____

_____

_____

_____

_____

_____

Did you ever cheat, or help someone else cheat? Describe. Did anyone find out? How did you feel about it afterwards?

_____

_____

_____

_____

_____

_____

How would you describe your study habits? Did you study with a buddy once a week, work for hours after school every day, or leave it all to last-minute cram sessions? How does this reflect your work habits today?

_____

_____

_____

_____

_____

_____

Did you ever have a tutor, or tutor someone else? How did you get along with your tutor or student? Did you get much out of the experience? Explain.

_____

_____

_____

_____

_____

_____

## Making History: Teen Idols

To the casual observer, this particular task may not exactly look like serious research — but perusing your own scrapbooks plus any magazines, albums, trading cards and movies you can find that date from your teenage years is a great way to reconnect with your teen idols, as well as the aspirations they represented to you. Refresh your memory about your teen idols:

**Music:** Whose album did you run out and buy as soon as it was released? Whose songs did you lip-synch in the bathroom mirror? Whose concert T-shirt did you proudly wear ragged? What was it about this musician you most wanted to emulate?

**Sports:** Whose action-shot poster did you have on the door to your room? Who was the athlete on that trading card you refused to trade, and kept propped up on your dresser? Whose number did you have on your own athletic jersey? Why did you identify so strongly with this athlete?

**Movies and TV:** Whose picture did you have up in your locker at school? Whose movie did you see twice in the same week? Whose fan club did you join? What was it about this star you admired most?

**Local heroes:** Whose every word did you hang on? Whose walk and talk did you mimic? Whose hard work inspired you to work harder yourself? How did that person influence your attitudes or ambitions?

_____

_____

_____

_____

_____

_____

_____

_____

_____

_____

_____

_____

_____

Next, clear out an evening to spend some quality time with the people you idolized as a teen. Stock up on movie rentals of all your favorite films as a teen, dig out your old scrapbooks, trading cards, yearbooks and record collection (remember records?!), and invite a few friends your age for an evening of teen idol worship. How do your idols look to you now – as cool as ever, or a little one-dimensional? Why? How did they influence your behavior back then? Who was your fashion icon in high school, and how did this person influence your choice of outfit, hairstyle, shoes? Were any of these fashion choices particularly regrettable? Did any of your teenage heroes inspire you to take risks or challenges in your own life – and if so, how did that experience shape you as a person? Which of your teen idols do you still admire most, and why?

_____

_____

_____

_____

_____

_____

_____

_____

_____

_____

_____

_____

_____

_____

_____

_____

_____

_____

_____

*The best way to keep children at home is to make the home atmosphere pleasant—and let the air out of the tires.*

— Dorothy Parker

## House rules

What was your curfew, if you ever had one? Did you ever break it, and if so, what were the consequences? Did your parents ever make an exception for school dances, summertime, and other occasions? Can you recall any arguments about this? In retrospect, do you think they were right to be so strict or relaxed about your curfew?

_____

_____

_____

_____

_____

_____

What were your family's rules about fighting? Can you remember ever hitting someone, or saying something you knew would seriously hurt someone's feelings? What were the consequences of your actions?

_____

_____

_____

_____

_____

_____

How did your parents feel about the music you listened to as a teen? How did you feel about theirs? Were you allowed to play your music at home or in the car?  How loudly? Was this a source of contention?

_____

_____

_____

_____

_____

Did you ever throw a party when your parents were away, or otherwise break the house rules when you thought you wouldn't get caught? Describe. Did the situation ever get out of control, and did you get in trouble? Were the police involved?

_____

_____

_____

_____

_____

_____

_____

_____

_____

_____

_____

What were your family's rules about dating – were you allowed to go out on weeknights, talk on the phone for hours, or visit in your bedroom with the door open a crack? Can you remember ever breaking or bending these rules? Describe.

_____

_____

_____

_____

_____

_____

_____

_____

_____

_____

_____

Children aren't happy without
something to ignore,
And that's what parents
were created for.

— Ogden Nash

## Ah, young love...

Who was your biggest crush in junior high and high school? Describe. Ever have a crush on someone you weren't supposed to – your best friend's boyfriend, a teacher, someone people told you was trouble? What ever came of those crushes? Do you know what happened to the people you had a crush on as a teenager?

_____

_____

_____

_____

_____

_____

What are your best and worst memories of school dances? Who were your dates at these events, and how did you pick them? Describe.

_____

_____

_____

_____

_____

Did you ever date someone whose race, religion, economic status, language, or social clique were different from yours? Did this difference pose any challenges for you, and if so, how did you handle it?

_____

_____

_____

_____

_____

Who was your first love? How did you meet and fall in love? How long were you together, and how did it end (if at all)? If you could say one thing to this person today, what would it be?

_____

_____

_____

_____

_____

_____

_____

_____

_____

_____

What do you remember about your first romantic kiss? Who was the kissee? Where and when did it occur? How would you describe it: short and sweet, a little sloppy around the edges, mildly painful due to the orthodonture involved?

_____

_____

_____

_____

_____

_____

_____

_____

_____

_____

Though I know he loves me,
Tonight my heart is sad;
His kiss was not so wonderful
As all the dreams I had.

— Sarah Teasdale

## A matter of trust

As a teenager, did you ever trust a friend with a big secret – a crush, a family problem, a scheme to sneak out of the house when you were grounded? What was the secret, and did your friend keep it?

_____

_____

_____

_____

_____

_____

Did you ever break a promise to a friend to keep a secret, or keep a friend's secret despite the consequences? Describe.

_____

_____

_____

_____

_____

_____

_____

Did you ever feel betrayed or abandoned by a friend as a teen? Why? Did you ever forgive this person? Why or why not?

_____

_____

_____

_____

_____

_____

Did you ever betray a friend back then, or drop an old friend to hang out with a new crowd? Describe. If you could talk to this person today, what would you say about it?

_____

_____

_____

_____

_____

_____

_____

Is there anything you borrowed as a teen that you never returned? What was it, and do you still have it? Why did you hang onto this item for so long, do you think?

_____

_____

_____

_____

_____

_____

_____

Did you ever try to be someone you really weren't? Explain. What convinced you to finally trust in yourself, and drop the act?

_____

_____

_____

_____

_____

_____

_____

**Focus on: Awkward moments**

What would you say was your most embarrassing moment as a teen – getting paralyzed with performance anxiety during a class presentation, accidentally blowing up your chemistry experiment, trying to pin a corsage on your prom date's strapless dress in front of her father? Describe. How did you deal with the situation? Did this experience make you more cautious about trying new things, or give you the perspective you needed to get over your fear of failure and take risks?

_____

_____

_____

_____

_____

_____

_____

_____

_____

_____

_____

_____

_____

_____

_____

_____

_____

_____

_____

_____

## Focus on: Awkward moments, cont.

Did anyone ever make fun of you in high school? Who? About what? Why do you think this person mocked you this way? How did you handle it at the time? What would you say to this person about that experience today? Did you ever purposely embarrass someone in high school yourself? If so, what exactly did you do or say and why? What would you like to say to this person about it today?

_____

_____

_____

_____

_____

_____

_____

_____

_____

_____

_____

_____

_____

_____

_____

_____

_____

_____

_____

_____

_____

_____

*If youth did not matter so much to itself,*
*it would never have the heart to go on.*

— Willa Cather

## Team player

Did you ever try out for or join an athletic team? Which one(s) and why? If you made the team, what did you like best and least about being on this team? How would you describe your coach? Can you still vividly recall any scenes from the team bus, playing field, or locker room? Describe.

---
---
---
---
---
---
---
---
---
---
---

What school activities did you participate in, if any: school yearbook, musicals, prom committee, school newspaper, jazz band? What inspired you to join, and what did you get out of the experience? What were the main advantages and drawbacks of your involvement?

---
---
---
---
---
---
---
---
---

Did you ever belong to any academic teams or school-sponsored groups – the debate team, French club, Future Farmers of America? How would you describe the high and low points of your time with this group?

_____

_____

_____

_____

_____

_____

Did you belong to any organizations outside of school, such as Girls or Boys Club, a debutant cotillion society, 4H, a religious youth group, Junior Achievement? Why did you join, and what do you think you learned from it? Please tell a story from your time there.

_____

_____

_____

_____

_____

_____

As a teenager, did you ever volunteer your time or talents – helping out at a hospital as a candy-striper, selling candy door to door to raise funds for a local charity, sewing costumes for the local opera company? What did you take away from the experience? Did it leave you with any skills or insights that are still helpful to you?

_____

_____

_____

_____

_____

## Growth spurts

As a teen, did you look older or younger than your age? Was this ever a problem for you? Describe. Can you think of a way it was helpful?

_____

_____

_____

_____

_____

_____

_____

Can you recall any situations you faced as a teenager that required you to grow up quickly? Describe. How did you handle it at the time? How has this experience contributed to the person you are today?

_____

_____

_____

_____

_____

_____

_____

When you went through tough times as a teen, what bit of advice or reassurance helped see you through it? Who gave you this helpful insight?

_____

_____

_____

_____

_____

_____

_____

What moments in your teenage years are you most proud of today? Least proud of? What did you learn from both these experiences?

_____

_____

_____

_____

_____

_____

_____

_____

_____

_____

When you finished high school, how did you feel? What experiences were you glad to put behind you? What were you most sad about leaving behind?

_____

_____

_____

_____

_____

_____

_____

_____

_____

_____

# CHAPTER FIVE

# Getting started: Young adulthood

*To conquer Fortune and everything else, begin by independence.*

— Jean-Jacques Rousseau

## On your own

How would you describe your first home away from home: a dorm room you shared with a messy roomie, a tiny apartment with a breathtaking view of a brick wall, a bunk in a military barracks with a footlocker for all your worldly belongings? What did you like best about your new place? What did you like least?

_____

_____

_____

_____

_____

_____

_____

_____

_____

_____

Describe the first car you ever bought. How did you choose it, and how much did it cost you? How would you describe it? Did it serve you well even on long road trips, or break down constantly? Were you fond of it, and did you give it a name?

_____

_____

_____

_____

_____

_____

_____

_____

_____

How did you handle your newfound freedom away from family and parental oversight? Did you take good care of yourself, or did you often deprive yourself or overindulge? Can you give an example of this? How did you finally decide to strike a better balance? Do you still have to keep this tendency in check today?

_____

_____

_____

_____

_____

_____

_____

_____

_____

How were you about paying bills back then? Did you ever have any financial crises brought on by car repairs, college tuition hikes, or long-distance phone calls to your boyfriend in Timbuktu? How did you deal with it? Did you take out student loans, hit up the folks, get a part-time job, pretend you weren't home when the credit card company called? How is this similar to or different from the way you manage your finances today?

_____

_____

_____

_____

_____

_____

_____

_____

## The old college try

Did you go to college? Why or why not? If you did, where did you go and how did you choose that school? Did it turn out to be a good choice for you? Why or why not? Did it help you discover a talent or cultivate an interest you might not have otherwise explored? Explain.

_____

_____

_____

_____

_____

_____

_____

_____

_____

_____

If you went to college, what was your major and why did you choose it? Did your choice of major have any bearing on your ultimate career direction? Explain. If you could turn back time and do it over, would you still choose that major? Why or why not?

_____

_____

_____

_____

_____

_____

_____

_____

_____

_____

Did you ever think about going back to school after you'd been working for a few years? What did you want to study? Did you do it? Why or why not? If so, briefly describe your experience.

_____

_____

_____

_____

_____

_____

_____

_____

_____

In college, did you meet anyone who played a pivotal role in your life, or turned out to be a lifelong friend or mentor? How did you meet, and what initially impressed you about this person? How do you think your life is different or better for having known this person?

_____

_____

_____

_____

_____

_____

_____

_____

_____

## The military

Did you go into the military? If you did, which branch of the armed forces were you in? Did it turn out to be a good choice for you? Why or why not? How did the experience change you?

If you chose not to serve in the armed forces, did you perform alternative service? If so, describe the experience.

_____

_____

_____

_____

_____

_____

If you did serve in the military, were you in combat? Explain. What are your strongest memories of that experience?

_____

_____

_____

_____

_____

_____

Did your service in the military have any bearing on your ultimate career direction? Explain. If you could turn back time and do it over, would you still have served in the armed forces? Why or why not?

_____

_____

_____

_____

_____

_____

## Focus on: Mighty mentors

Who are the people who had the most influence on you in your early adulthood?
Consider whose example or advice you followed at pivotal moments in your young adult
life – an older sibling, a professor, a friend of the family, the resident advisor for your
dorm, a slightly more experienced co-worker, a religious advisor? Think about who shaped
your thinking in the following areas:

**Studies:** Who influenced your choice of courses or major at college?

**Career:** Who did you turn to for moral support before a critical job interview, or consult
before making a major career switch?

**Relationships:** When you wanted to impress a certain someone, who did you hit up for
advice? What about when you were trying to get over a tough breakup?

**Faith:** Is there a person who helped you find hope or meaning in your life after a loss or
setback?

**Focus on: Mighty mentors, cont.**

How exactly did this mentor help you? Did you ever model your behavior on this person's? Can you recall this person giving you any crucial insight or bit of advice? Did this person show unwavering faith in you when you had a crisis of confidence, or tell you something you didn't want to hear but needed to? Explain.

_____

_____

_____

_____

_____

_____

_____

_____

_____

_____

_____

_____

_____

_____

_____

_____

_____

_____

_____

_____

_____

_____

_____

_____

## Finding your direction

What single experience as a young person proved to be the most formative for you? Was it studying abroad in India, being stationed in Germany, joining a women's group, looking after your ailing grandmother? Describe. What important insights did you gain from this experience? How would you describe the long-term impact this experience had on your life?

_____

_____

_____

_____

_____

_____

_____

_____

_____

_____

What's the best piece of constructive criticism you got as a young person? Who gave it to you? Under what circumstances? What potentially embarrassing mistakes and unnecessary anguish do you think this has saved you over the years? Explain.

_____

_____

_____

_____

_____

_____

_____

_____

_____

Can you think of the first time you were given an opportunity to shine? Was it your first job as a pilot, that time you were invited to play piano in a jazz quartet, or in veterinary school when you were specially selected to treat a sick giraffe? Who gave you this big break? How did you react when you were told the good news?

_____

_____

_____

_____

_____

_____

Did you ever get your hopes up about a dream job, scholarship, promotion, or some other golden opportunity, only to be disappointed? Describe. How did you handle the disappointment at the time?

_____

_____

_____

_____

_____

In retrospect, what alternative path did you pursue that you might not have if this opportunity had landed in your lap? Did this detour lead you to another opportunity that turned out to be even better for you?

_____

_____

_____

_____

_____

*How often I found where
I should be going only by setting
out for somewhere else.*

— R. Buckminster Fuller

## Aspirations

When you were first starting out in your career, what did you hope to achieve in the course of your career? Did any of these goals prove to be much harder to realize than you thought they were going to be? Explain. Which of these goals did you achieve? How? Which became less important with time? Why?

_____

_____

_____

_____

_____

_____

_____

_____

_____

_____

Did you have any goals back then with regards to family, such as giving your parents a more comfortable life or having at least four children? Why? What steps did you take to help make this happen, if any? Did you attain your goal, or was there a change in plan? Explain. If you attained this goal, was it everything you hoped it would be, or not quite?

_____

_____

_____

_____

_____

_____

_____

_____

Did you have any creative aspirations at the time – to learn to dance flamenco, write a love poem, make at least one vase in ceramics class that wasn't lopsided? Which of these did you actively pursue, and which did you abandon? Why? What was the reward for your creative efforts – a newfound confidence, a romantic evening, a vase that didn't fall over?

_____

_____

_____

_____

_____

_____

_____

_____

_____

Back in those days, what did you most want to change about the world? Were there laws you thought needed to be passed, or social mores you thought needed to change with the times? What did you do about it? Looking back, how do you feel about your actions — or inaction?

_____

_____

_____

_____

_____

_____

_____

_____

_____

*That's what being young is all about.*
*You have the courage and daring to*
*think you can make a difference.*

— *Ruby Dee*

## Personal convictions

What political causes did you support at this age? How were your political convictions similar to or different from the political beliefs of others in your family? Can you recall getting into any political arguments with relatives, friends, professors, or coworkers? Describe.

_____

_____

_____

_____

_____

_____

_____

What religious beliefs did you adopt as a young person? Why did these feel right to you at the time? Do you still believe them?

_____

_____

_____

_____

_____

_____

_____

What religious perspectives did you reject back then, and why? Have you changed your tune about these beliefs? Why or why not?

_____

_____

_____

_____

_____

_____

_____

Can you think of any ethical dilemmas you faced at this young age – confronting a friend about his cheating ways, taking a job you knew you'd leave in a matter of months, fighting a war you didn't personally support? What did you ultimately decide to do? Looking back now, do you think you made the right decision for your conscience? Why or why not?

_____

_____

_____

_____

_____

_____

_____

_____

_____

_____

Can you recall ever taking a stand on a political, religious or ethical issue that came at a personal cost to you – falling out with a family member, forfeiting a job opportunity, getting in trouble with the law or campus authorities for protesting? Describe. What inspired you to take this stand? How do you feel about it today?

_____

_____

_____

_____

_____

_____

_____

_____

_____

_____

Forget conventionalisms; forget what the world thinks of you stepping out of your place; think your best thoughts, speak your best words, do your best works, looking to your own conscience for approval.

— Susan B. Anthony

## Career choices

How would you describe your first full-time job? How did you hear about the position, and what can you recall about your job interview? Did the work interest you, or was it just a way to pay the bills while you figured out what you really wanted to do? Did you have a good relationship with your boss? Why or why not?

_____
_____
_____
_____
_____
_____
_____
_____
_____
_____

Why did you leave your first job? Did you leave on good terms? Why or why not? What friendships or contacts did you maintain even after you left, and what role have these people played in your life?

_____
_____
_____
_____
_____
_____
_____
_____
_____
_____

What would you say was the first major turning point in your career – being promoted to management, deciding to go to graduate school, getting laid off by your company? How did this event lead you in a direction you hadn't anticipated, or move you closer to your career goals?

_____

_____

_____

_____

_____

_____

_____

_____

_____

What is the worst job you ever had when you were getting started in your career? What made it so difficult – tedious tasks, long hours, impossible boss? How long did you last in this position, and what finally made you move on to greener pastures?

_____

_____

_____

_____

_____

_____

_____

_____

_____

## Hangouts

What were your favorite places to hang out with friends back then – a student lounge with big couches, a diner where they served pancakes until midnight, a neighborhood bar, a cafe where they gave free coffee refills? Can you recall any three-hour conversations or plots you hatched there? Describe.

_____

_____

_____

_____

_____

_____

_____

_____

_____

What were your favorite entertainment venues? Was there a club where your favorite bands played, a park where everyone roller-skated on weekends, a theater or movie palace with bargain matinees? Describe one particularly memorable experience at this venue.

_____

_____

_____

_____

_____

_____

_____

_____

_____

Besides your own, whose home did you visit most often back then? Was this the home of a best friend, a girlfriend, a boyfriend, a relative? Did you stay there so often people thought you lived there? Describe this place. Why did you feel so at home there? What is your strongest memory of this place?

_____

_____

_____

_____

_____

_____

_____

_____

_____

_____

Back then, where was your favorite place to go on vacation or for weekend getaways? Did you go to a lakeside cabin that belonged to your best friend's parents, a national park where you pitched your tent and subsisted on roasted marshmallows, or an uncrowded beach with a particularly attractive lifeguard? What's the fondest memory you have of this place?

_____

_____

_____

_____

_____

_____

_____

_____

## The company you keep

Did you have any roommates when you first moved away from home? Who were they, and how did you meet them? How did you get along? Can you recall a highlight of your time living under the same roof? Describe.

_____

_____

_____

_____

_____

_____

_____

_____

_____

Who were your closest friends after you moved away from home? Who were the first new friends you made back then, and why do you think you hit it off so well? Did you keep in touch with any of your friends from back home? Who? Why?

_____

_____

_____

_____

_____

_____

_____

_____

_____

_____

How did you get along with your coworkers back in those days — did you spend every weekend with friends from work, hang out with the other assistant managers at lunch, or come up with any excuse to avoid company picnics? Why?

_____

_____

_____

_____

_____

_____

_____

_____

_____

_____

Was there any one coworker at your first job you became particularly close to? What about one you felt particular antipathy towards? Why?

_____

_____

_____

_____

_____

_____

_____

_____

_____

_____

*We cannot live only for ourselves. A thousand fibers connect us with our fellow men; and among those fibers, as sympathetic threads, our actions run as causes, and they come back to us as effects.*

— Herman Melville

## Instant memories: Fan mail

Name five people whom you admired deeply as a young adult, and share a few words explaining what you so admired about each one. The first people that come to mind might be public figures who you knew only through their work – an author, a political figure, a religious leader. But be sure you also include people you knew personally – a professor who always made you think, a cousin who gave up an investment banking career to work with refugees, a friend who was equally talented in physics and filmmaking.

## Instant memories: Fan mail, cont.

Next, jot down a few words about how each person inspired you then and now. If you can track down a current address for one or more of these people (or their representatives, in the case of public figures), send them a card or letter describing the inspiration you gained from their work. If any of them still work at the place where you met, you might send a copy of your compliments to that person's boss for added impact. If the person is deceased, you might send it to a surviving family member who would be appreciative of your comments. How did it feel to send that fan mail? If you get a response, write about it below too.

_____

_____

_____

_____

_____

_____

_____

_____

_____

_____

_____

_____

_____

_____

_____

_____

_____

_____

_____

*Two things I always knew about you*
*one that you are smart*
*two that you are a swell guy*
*Love Dad.*

*— Telegram from Joseph Kennedy*
*to his son John Fitzgerald Kennedy*

## Hot pursuits

How did you usually approach someone for a date back then, or let a person know when you were interested? How successful were these tactics? What's the worst pickup line you ever heard, or actually tried yourself?

\
\
\
\
\
\
\

Can you remember the first time you declared your love for another person? Who was the lucky person, and what were the circumstances? How was it received?

\
\
\
\
\
\
\

What was the first time you heard those three magic words yourself? Describe.

\
\
\
\
\
\
\

What was your biggest heartbreak back then – a good relationship gone bad, an unrequited love, a secret affair with someone already attached? Explain. What did you do that helped you get over it: go out dancing with friends, write in your journal, take up martial arts? Can you recall any especially good advice that helped to see you through this tough time?

_____

_____

_____

_____

_____

_____

_____

_____

_____

_____

Back when you were still very young, did you ever meet someone you thought was not only special, but might actually be The One for you? What gave you this feeling? Did you pursue this person? Were you right?

_____

_____

_____

_____

_____

_____

_____

_____

_____

_____

*There's someone out there for everyone — even if you need a pickaxe, a compass, and night goggles to find them.*

— Steve Martin

## Tastes in the making

What music moved you most back then – rock, big band, soul music, bluegrass? Are there songs you loved then that still sound great to you today? Which ones? What memories do they bring back to you?

_____

_____

_____

_____

_____

_____

_____

Are there any memories of concerts or shows you saw back then that are still clear in your mind today? Describe.

_____

_____

_____

_____

_____

_____

Can you recall the first time as an adult that a work of art took your breath away? What was it about this piece that so impressed and moved you? Did something about it strike you as intimately familiar, or completely original? Do you still get that feeling from looking at it today?

_____

_____

_____

_____

_____

_____

Can you think of a book back then that opened up new horizons for you, or changed your thinking about the world in some way? Explain. Why do you think this book had such a powerful effect on you? If you have a favorite line or phrase from this book, what is it?

_____

_____

_____

_____

_____

_____

_____

Did you have a favorite film at this time of your life? What do you get out of watching this film now that you didn't back then?

_____

_____

_____

_____

_____

_____

_____

What new foods did you discover after you moved away from home? How was your cooking? Were you on your way to becoming a gourmet chef already, or were you a disaster in the kitchen? What was a typical meal for you back then?

_____

_____

_____

_____

_____

_____

# CHAPTER SIX

# Hitting your stride: Evolution Years

*We touch the moment*
*with our fingers,*
*we cut it*
*to size,*
*we direct its blooming.*
*It's living, it's alive:*
*It brings nothing from yesterday that*
*can't be redeemed*

*— Pablo Neruda*

## Romantic intrigue

Who would you say was your first serious romantic relationship? How did you meet?

_____

_____

_____

_____

_____

_____

_____

How long were you together before you decided this was the one for you, or went your separate ways? What led you to this decision?

_____

_____

_____

_____

_____

_____

_____

How many serious relationships would you say you've had since that first one (if any)? What are your best and worst memories from these relationships? What did you learn from each of these about yourself, and about relationships?

_____

_____

_____

_____

_____

_____

_____

Is there any one relationship you found particularly difficult to let go? Which one, and why? What helped you to move on?

_____

_____

_____

_____

_____

_____

_____

_____

_____

_____

Did you ever break off an engagement or split up with someone after you'd been together a long time? Why? How did you do it? If you had it to do all over again, would you handle it differently? How?

_____

_____

_____

_____

_____

_____

_____

_____

_____

_____

## Marriage and commitment

Was there someone at this time in your life you felt was the one for you? How did you meet? Did you decide to get married? Why or why not?

_____

_____

_____

_____

_____

_____

If you did get married, who popped the question, and how? What do you remember about the proposal? Was the answer an immediate yes, or did it take some convincing?

_____

_____

_____

_____

_____

_____

Can you remember the first time you met the family of your significant other? Describe. What were your impressions of them? What kind of impression do you think you made on them? How have these impressions been confirmed or changed over time?

_____

_____

_____

_____

_____

_____

If you celebrated your commitment with a wedding or ceremony, describe the big day. What important people in your life were there to show their love and support? What was the ceremony like? The reception? What are your most lasting memories of this day? If you went on a honeymoon, where did you go and how was it?

_____

_____

_____

_____

_____

_____

_____

_____

_____

If you've been married more than once, what would you say was the best part of your first marriage? What about the most serious problem? How would you say your subsequent marriage(s) turned out to be an improvement on this first one?

_____

_____

_____

_____

_____

_____

_____

_____

_____

*No human relation gives one possession in another — every two souls are absolutely different. In friendship or in love, the two side by side raise hands together to find what one cannot reach alone.*

— Khalil Gibran

## Career advancement

Did you ever switch careers? What led you to make this change? Was it a tough or surprisingly smooth transition? Did you find your new line of work more personally fulfilling? Why or why not?

_____

_____

_____

_____

_____

_____

_____

_____

_____

Can you recall the first time you realized you were making a name for yourself in your career? How did it happen – did you earn a major promotion, did a complete stranger compliment you on your work, were you invited to speak at an event as an expert in your field? Describe. Who were the first people you told about it? What were their responses?

_____

_____

_____

_____

_____

_____

_____

_____

_____

Can you think of any major challenges you confronted as you advanced in your career – losing your job, a boss who took credit for your work, bumping up against stereotypes in your workplace? Explain. How did you deal with these setbacks?

_____

_____

_____

_____

_____

_____

_____

_____

_____

Did you ever strike out on your own and start your own business? How did you scrape together the capital you needed? Who were your first clients? What about your first partners or employees? What did you learn from the experience about your own strengths and shortcomings?

_____

_____

_____

_____

_____

_____

_____

_____

_____

## Downtime

At this time in your life, how much vacation time did you have? How did you usually spend your holidays – taking road trips with friends or siblings, cooking elaborate meals for your family, teaching the kids to swim or ski? Would you have preferred to spend your holidays some other way? Why or why not?

_____

_____

_____

_____

_____

_____

_____

_____

_____

_____

What would you say was the best vacation or outing you ever organized for your family? Describe. Was it the special museum exhibit on ancient Egyptian mummies, that county fair where you won the pie-eating contest, or the Hawaiian dream vacation complete with ukulele lessons?

_____

_____

_____

_____

_____

_____

_____

_____

_____

At this busy time in your life, how did you spend most of your leisure time – catching up on house repairs, taking the kids to dance classes across town, finally returning friends' phone calls?

_____

_____

_____

_____

_____

_____

How much actual leisure were you able to squeeze in given all your responsibilities? Was there a kind soul who helped you out, or made sure you took a breather once in a while?

_____

_____

_____

_____

_____

_____

When were you able to make time just for yourself – on the train ride to work, after everyone else in the house went to sleep, on Sunday afternoons after the housework was done? How did you spend that precious time?

_____

_____

_____

_____

_____

_____

One ought, every day at least, to hear a little song, read a good poem, see a fine picture and, if possible, speak a few reasonable words.

— Johann Wolfgang von Goethe

## Making history: Great performances

Even though you may not have realized it at the time, you may have witnessed an earth-shaking cultural phenomenon or two in your day. Remember the first time you heard the Beatles on the radio, or saw Hank Aaron step up to bat, or worried that Martha Graham would hurt herself if she kept throwing herself around the floor like that in the middle of a dance? Look through your scrapbooks and see if you find any ticket stubs or other memorabilia from shows, movies and concerts. What do you remember thinking about these performances at the time – maybe "No one's going to want to come with me to a concert at some farm near Woodstock," or perhaps "That little Judy Garland is not half bad"? Did history prove you right or wrong, do you think?

If you can't think of any great performances you witnessed, do a little historical research to jog your memory. Check out the arts and entertainment sections of magazines and newspapers, and read the reviews. Do you remember your own assessment of any of these shows at the time they came out?

_____

_____

_____

_____

_____

_____

_____

_____

_____

_____

_____

_____

_____

_____

_____

_____

_____

## Make yourself at home

Did you make any major moves at this time in your life – moving across the country for a new job, moving back to your home state to be closer to family, moving to another city or country to pursue a relationship? How did this move change your life for the better, and for the worse? Describe.

_____
_____
_____
_____
_____
_____
_____

What was the first home you shared with a significant other? Where was it located? What did it look like? What were your favorite and least favorite things about it?

_____
_____
_____
_____
_____
_____
_____

What did you do to make your first place together feel like home – invite the neighbors over for a barbecue, build in bookshelves, paint the place pink?

_____
_____
_____
_____
_____
_____

At the time, did you and your loved one have differences of opinion about what you wanted in a home – proximity to work, a pool table, a place to put your extensive cactus collection? How did you resolve these differences?

_____

_____

_____

_____

_____

_____

_____

_____

_____

_____

How did you and your significant other adjust to sharing a home and life together? What kinds of arguments arose initially? How did you resolve these conflicts? When did it become clear to you that this relationship was meant to last – or wasn't?

_____

_____

_____

_____

_____

_____

_____

_____

_____

*Nothing is built on stone;
all is built on sand, but we must
build as if the sand were stone.*

— *Jorge Luis Borges*

## Putting down roots

Where is the first place you lived as an adult where you felt you really belonged? Why? What made you feel so at home in that neighborhood, town, or part of the country?

_____

_____

_____

_____

_____

_____

_____

_____

_____

When you first settled in this place, what were your favorite places to hang out, eat, shop? Did you become friendly with any of the proprietors, employees, or fellow customers at these neighborhood joints? Who? Can you recall any particularly memorable interactions you had?

_____

_____

_____

_____

_____

_____

_____

_____

_____

Did you find a place of worship as an adult where you felt at home? What was it about this place and the people you met there that put you at ease?

_____

_____

_____

_____

_____

_____

_____

Can you think of neighbors who made you feel right at home in a new neighborhood, or a co-worker who graciously showed you the ropes at a new job? How did this make your neighborhood or workplace a more comfortable, pleasant place to be? Have you ever passed on the favor to new neighbors or co-workers? Describe.

_____

_____

_____

_____

_____

_____

How did you first get involved with your local community – volunteering at the public library, baking cookies for a PTA charity bazaar, converting an abandoned building into a new community center? How did this lead to further involvement with your community?

_____

_____

_____

_____

_____

## Traveling rocky roads

Can you remember the first devastating emotional loss you experienced? Describe the circumstances. How did you find the strength to make it through this difficult time? Who came through for you in your time of need?

_____

_____

_____

_____

_____

_____

_____

_____

Were you ever separated or divorced? What do you think caused this rift? Was it difficult to adjust to living without a significant other at first? If so, how? If not, why do you think life improved for you so after the separation?

_____

_____

_____

_____

_____

_____

_____

_____

Did you ever struggle with addiction or other self-destructive behaviors? Can you give an example of this? Who else did your behavior affect? How did you recognize the problem and begin to address it? Was there anyone who called you on your problem, and then stood by you as you got your life back together?

_____

_____

_____

_____

_____

_____

_____

_____

_____

_____

Did you ever go through what you would consider a mid-life crisis? What brought it on? What were the symptoms? How did you recognize it for what it was, and get beyond it?

_____

_____

_____

_____

_____

_____

_____

_____

_____

## Striking compromises

What would you say are the most significant compromises you made back then to help build a relationship – moving across country to be with your loved one, learning to speak her native language, letting your significant other have the bigger closet to accommodate all his shoes? How did you arrive at that compromise? Have you ever regretted it? Why or why not?

_____

_____

_____

_____

_____

_____

_____

_____

What major compromises did your loved one make to accommodate you back then – supporting you during law school, spending holidays with your folks in Dubuque, looking after the kids on poker nights? How do you think this deepened your relationship at the time? What did these compromises make possible for you longer-term – a mid-life career change, a strong relationship with your parents in their later years, less stress?

_____

_____

_____

_____

_____

_____

_____

_____

Can you think of a time you compromised your ethics or values? Did you cheat on your taxes, do work you considered sleazy or unethical, laugh at a crass ethnic joke your boss made? Why? How did you feel about it at the time, and how do you feel about it now?

_____

_____

_____

_____

_____

_____

_____

_____

_____

At this time in your life, what would you say is the biggest compromise you made to accommodate your family? Was it taking time off work so you could spend time with a sibling experiencing tough times, going to school at night so you could one day provide your kids with a college education, or downshifting to part-time work so you could take care of an aging parent? How has this enriched your family's life? Has this enriched your own life?

_____

_____

_____

_____

_____

_____

_____

_____

## Instant memories: Fly solo

Think of five places near and far that you wanted to go at this busy time in your life, but never got around to visiting due to your many responsibilities. These places could be as near as the local opera house, or as far away as Macchu Picchu. List each place below, along with a few words explaining what fascinated you about each place.

_____

_____

_____

_____

_____

_____

_____

_____

_____

_____

_____

_____

_____

_____

_____

_____

_____

_____

_____

_____

_____

_____

# CHAPTER SEVEN

# Doing for others: Parenting and caretaking

*From what we get, we can
make a living; what we give,
however, makes a life.*

— Arthur Ashe

## Great expectations

If you or your significant other ever became pregnant, do you remember how you found out about that first pregnancy? Was the pregnancy a surprise or planned? What was your initial reaction? What was your partner's reaction? What was the immediate effect on your lives?

_____

_____

_____

_____

_____

_____

_____

_____

_____

What are your strongest memories of that first pregnancy? Were there any complications or concerns? What do you remember about the prenatal visits and ultrasounds?

_____

_____

_____

_____

_____

_____

_____

_____

_____

How many times did you or your significant other become pregnant, and how many children did you have together? What are your strongest memories of these other pregnancies?

_____

_____

_____

_____

_____

_____

Did you or your partner ever have any miscarriages or experience difficulty conceiving? How did this affect you and your partner? How did this experience change your life plans? How do you think it changed your family?

_____

_____

_____

_____

_____

_____

If you were ever pregnant, do any small acts of kindness during your pregnancy stand out in your mind – a neighbor throwing you a baby shower, a complete stranger offering to carry your groceries, an hour-long foot massage from your partner? Describe.

_____

_____

_____

_____

_____

*Her pregnancy was like a load that held her down, and yet like a hand that pulled her to her feet.*

— Edith Wharton

## Small wonders

If you had children, what can you recall about the circumstances of each child's birth? Where were you and your partner when the labor pains began? How long did the labor last? What kind of medical assistance did you have for the birth? Were there any complications? Who was in the waiting room?

_____

_____

_____

_____

_____

_____

_____

_____

_____

_____

How did you choose each of your children's first and middle names? Did you and your partner agree on the name right away, or did it take some serious negotiation? Given how your children's personalities have developed, do you think the names you chose for them actually suit them? Why or why not?

_____

_____

_____

_____

_____

_____

_____

_____

_____

As a new parent, what was the hardest personal adjustment you had to make? What do you know now that you wish you'd known then about becoming a parent?

_____

_____

_____

_____

_____

_____

_____

_____

_____

What are your favorite memories of each of your children as babies or toddlers? Can you recall an especially funny remark, a little dance whenever cookies were offered, a touching moment with an older sibling?  Describe.

_____

_____

_____

_____

_____

_____

_____

_____

_____

## Tiny terrors

Can you remember any of your children making a smart-aleck remark or sassing back when they were little? Describe the situation, and your reaction. Were you amused, embarrassed, outwardly distressed but inwardly proud?

_____

_____

_____

_____

_____

_____

_____

_____

_____

_____

Do you think the smart remark or naughty behavior was an indicator of the child's personality, just a phase, or a rare flare-up? Explain.

_____

_____

_____

_____

_____

_____

_____

_____

_____

How did you discipline your children? Did you ever have a hard time enforcing rules or following through with consequences? Did you ever regret disciplining your children as much as you did, or not disciplining your children enough? Explain.

_____

_____

_____

_____

_____

_____

_____

_____

_____

_____

Do you remember any particularly scary moments when your children were babies or toddlers – a serious illness, a sudden disappearance in a grocery store, a toy that became lunch? How did you respond to this crisis?

_____

_____

_____

_____

_____

_____

_____

_____

_____

## It takes a village...

Other than any children of your own, what children have been important to you in your adult life – beloved nieces or nephews, foster children, grandchildren, favorite neighbors, god-daughters or god-sons, close friends' kids? Why?

_____

_____

_____

_____

_____

_____

_____

What pivotal moments did you witness in their lives? What was your role in this event or decision?

_____

_____

_____

_____

_____

_____

_____

What have you learned from each of these important children in your life? What do you hope they have learned from you?

_____

_____

_____

_____

_____

_____

_____

Other than you and your significant other, what other adults played an important role in your children's lives – babysitters, grandparents, siblings, teachers? What specific positive influence do you think they've had on your kids? What about negative influences?

_____

_____

_____

_____

_____

_____

_____

_____

_____

_____

Who would you most like to thank for their support or help in raising your children? Why?

_____

_____

_____

_____

_____

_____

_____

_____

_____

_____

_____

## Making history: Family reunions

Looking through old family memorabilia, you'll probably find photos of family get-togethers or reunions over the years. Does your family have a tradition of:

**Holiday extravaganzas,** with special family rituals, fancy meals, and home-made presents?

**Weekend getaways** by a lake just for the grown siblings, where no one ever seemed to catch any fish?

**A five-course dinner** every weekend for the entire extended family and countless cousins, where your great-aunt always sat at the head of the table?

**A summer holiday** at the family's favorite beach or campsite, where the kids told ghost stories or performed their own plays for the parents?

What specifics do you recall about these family get-togethers, and what do others in your family remember or know about them? Were there certain traditions or customs at these events — a stately great-aunt who always dressed for dinner, an all-night game of Scrabble among the adults, kids always trying to pinch each other under the dinner table? Were there special treats, performances, or elaborate meals cooked for the occasion? Describe. Which were your favorite and least favorite family traditions at these events?

_____

_____

_____

_____

_____

_____

_____

_____

_____

_____

_____

_____

_____

_____

_____

Now that you've captured the details of family occasions of yore, plan an old-fashioned family get-together for sometime in the next six months. This is a prime opportunity to revive a few of the family traditions you described above, and pass them on to your children and grandchildren. Some suggestions:

**Location:** Plan to meet at a favorite family spot, or at a historic locale that's important in your family history – such as Gettysburg, where your great-great-great-grandfather died.

**Food:** Dig up the recipe for your great-grandmother's rich yellow cake.

**Entertainment:** Find the sheet music to the song your great-uncle always used to sing at family gatherings, and learn to sing it or play it.

**Outings:** Go sailing in honor of your great-great-grandfather, the legendary sea captain.

**Attire:** Wear your grandfather's holiday bow tie, or your great-aunt's enormous feathered hat.

Set a date as soon as possible with your family members and children to make sure they can attend, and invite them to contribute their own memories to the occasion. Then after the big event, capture your favorite memories of it below.

_____

_____

_____

_____

_____

_____

_____

_____

_____

_____

_____

_____

_____

_____

_____

_____

_____

## Parental guidance

How was the way you raised your kids similar to the way you were raised? How was it different?

_____

_____

_____

_____

_____

_____

_____

_____

_____

_____

Did you ever have any disagreements with your significant other about how to raise the children? Describe.

_____

_____

_____

_____

_____

_____

_____

_____

_____

What role models or peers did you rely on most for parenting inspiration or advice? What would you say is the most important lesson about parenting you learned from each of these people?

_____

_____

_____

_____

_____

_____

What do you think was the worst piece of parenting advice you were ever given? Describe. Why do you think this advice is so wrong?

_____

_____

_____

_____

_____

_____

What one useful piece of parenting advice would you like to offer future generations of parents?

_____

_____

_____

_____

_____

_____

## Coming of age

If you've already raised a child into young adulthood, what are your strongest memories of the experience? How was the transition for your child? How was it for you?

_____

_____

_____

_____

_____

_____

_____

_____

_____

_____

Do you think your kids had an easier time with adolescence than you did? Why or why not?

_____

_____

_____

_____

_____

_____

_____

_____

_____

_____

When did you realize your offspring was no longer a child, but a young adult? Was there a particular event that brought on this realization – a school dance, a first job, a clash of the wills over the use of the family car? How did you react at the time?

_____

_____

_____

_____

_____

_____

_____

_____

_____

_____

If your children have already left home, how did you adjust to not having them around? Was life easier, busier, more comfortable or stressful? Why?

_____

_____

_____

_____

_____

_____

_____

_____

_____

_____

## Instant memories: Perfect timing

There's no time like the present to record your memories of your children. Using the categories below, note the time and date of events you recall in the life of each child, and describe the event as you recall it. Be sure to include

**Milestones:** Birth date, first words, first day at school, first job, first date?

_____

_____

_____

_____

_____

_____

**Triumphs:** Spelling bees, home runs, school plays, science fairs, college honors, professional recognition?

_____

_____

_____

_____

_____

_____

**Trials:** Broken arm, lost pet, tough teacher, layoffs, personal tragedy?

_____

_____

_____

_____

_____

_____

**Turning points:** Graduation, marriage, promotion, children, major moves?

_____

_____

_____

_____

_____

**Breakthroughs:** Discoveries, recoveries, leadership?

_____

_____

_____

_____

_____

**Travel:** Holiday vacation, summer camp, trip abroad?

_____

_____

_____

_____

**Favorite times together:** reading a bedtime story, a Saturday outing, a long talk on the way to college?

_____

_____

_____

_____

Next, plot the key dates and descriptions outlined above for each of your children along a separate timeline. You can do this either on a computer, or by hand on a long scroll of paper. Once you're finished, add a title at the top that reads:

**_____ : A Lifetime of Memories by _____**
     [child's name]                                    [your name]

Then share your handiwork with the person who inspired it: your son or daughter. Make an occasion of it, and present your work to each child at a special birthday, holiday, wedding shower or another life event. You might tie it with a ribbon and give it as a present, frame it to make it look official, or tack it up on a wall with extra paper and pens so that others can add their memories to the timeline too. Afterwards, add a few words about this experience below. How was your gift received? How did you feel about giving it?

_____

_____

_____

_____

_____

_____

_____

_____

_____

_____

_____

_____

_____

_____

## Sick days

Did you ever look after sick children? How did you try to make them well, or at least feel better? Describe.

_____

_____

_____

_____

_____

_____

_____

_____

_____

_____

Can you recall looking after a sick relative, or making frequent visits to someone who was unwell or elderly? How did you come to care for this person? What did you do for this loved one?

_____

_____

_____

_____

_____

_____

_____

_____

_____

Did you ever lose someone to an illness or injury? Where were you when it happened —trying to sleep in the waiting room, by the bedside, out of town on a much-needed vacation? Did you get a chance to say goodbye? If so, what did you say? If not, what would you like to have said?

_____

_____

_____

_____

_____

_____

_____

_____

_____

_____

Who looked after you when you were sick — a doting friend, a relative, a significant other? What did this person do for you? What is the nicest thing this person ever did for you?

_____

_____

_____

_____

_____

_____

_____

_____

_____

What does love look like? It has the hands to help others. It has the feet to hasten to the poor and needy. It has eyes to see misery and want. It has the ears to hear the sighs and sorrows of men. That is what love looks like.

— St. Augustine

## True devotion

If you had kids, describe your approach to parenting. What was your greatest challenge as a parent or stepparent, and how did you deal with it?

_____

_____

_____

_____

_____

_____

_____

Can you think of a time when you were at your best as a parent? Describe.

_____

_____

_____

_____

_____

_____

_____

What about a time when you think you could have done a better job of parenting? What do you think you learned from the experience? Have you tried to make it up to your kids over the years? If so, how?

_____

_____

_____

_____

_____

_____

_____

If you were to praise each of your children, what would you say? Have you ever shared these compliments with your children? Why or why not?

_____

_____

_____

_____

_____

_____

_____

_____

_____

What do you think your children would say about you as a parent? What specific praise do you think they'd offer? What criticism?

_____

_____

_____

_____

_____

_____

_____

_____

Besides parenting, what other caretaker roles have you taken on—looking after your parents as they grew older, making speccial trips to visit sick relatives or friends?

_____

_____

_____

_____

_____

_____

_____

_____

_____

_____

_____

_____

_____

_____

_____

_____

_____

_____

_____

_____

_____

_____

_____

# CHAPTER EIGHT

# Making Your Mark: Maturity

*What lies behind us and what lies before us are tiny matters compared to what lies within us.*

*— Ralph Waldo Emerson*

## Watershed moments

Can you recall taking on a challenge where no one – including you – really expected you'd succeed, and you did? Can you think of a time when even you thought you were crazy for trying? What motivated you to stick with it?

_____

_____

_____

_____

_____

_____

_____

_____

_____

Can you think of a time you reestablished a relationship you were convinced was lost to you after one too many unreturned letters, unresolved conflicts, or years gone by between visits?

_____

_____

_____

_____

_____

_____

_____

_____

_____

If you had to name one subject you've learned so much about over the years that you could probably write a book about it, what would it be? How did you end up accumulating so much knowledge in this area? Did it inspire you to deepen your expertise in other areas?

_____

_____

_____

_____

_____

_____

_____

_____

_____

_____

What one original idea or invention of yours always seems to impress people? How has this successful venture encouraged you to take unconventional approaches to other problems? Can you give an example?

_____

_____

_____

_____

_____

_____

_____

_____

_____

*They say that time changes things, but actually you have to change them yourself.*

— Andy Warhol

## Surviving and thriving

Have you ever been through a natural disaster – tornado, earthquake, flood, fire? Describe. How did you respond, and make it through this harrowing event? Were you able to help anyone else, or were you lucky to escape with your own life? Explain.

---
---
---
---
---
---
---
---
---

As an adult, did you experience a loss so debilitating you feared you might never recover from it? Can you recall a low point when you thought you wouldn't make it? What was the turning point for you, when rebuilding your life began to seem possible?

---
---
---
---
---
---
---
---
---

In your adult life, have you ever had to deal with violence – your own, someone else's, or both? How was this violence manifested: crimes, war, abuse? Explain. What physical and emotional toll did it take on you, and others around you? How has this experience changed how you deal with violence?

_____

_____

_____

_____

_____

_____

_____

_____

_____

What serious illness or health scares have you had to contend with in your adult life? How has this experience changed your approach to your health? Did this health problem get you thinking about how you could work around physical limitations, or lead you to rearrange your personal priorities in any way? Describe.

_____

_____

_____

_____

_____

_____

_____

_____

*The world breaks everyone and afterward many are strong at the broken places.*

— Ernest Hemingway

## Creative growth

As an adult, did you ever surprise yourself by discovering a creative ability you never knew you had – culinary prowess, photography, knitting, something else? What led to this discovery? Did you get ambitious when you had to whip up a dish for a potluck? Did you find yourself flipping through magazines saying, "I bet I could take photographs that look this good"? Did you find exquisite yarn you knew you just had to knit? Describe.

_____

_____

_____

_____

_____

_____

Did you ever perform in front of others as an adult? Did you play music, act in a play, or sing in a choir, musical or opera? Were you nervous? Was anyone there to cheer you on? What was the best part of the experience for you? What performances have you been in since that first one, if any? How has performing changed you?

_____

_____

_____

_____

_____

What artistic creation are you most proud to have made as an adult—a sculpture, quilt, video, something else? What details are you particularly proud of in this piece? What do you remember about the process of making it—did you wind up covered in clay from head to toe, stay up all night sewing, shoot it with the help of a couple of friends? Describe. Of all the comments you ever got on this piece, which is your favorite?

_____

_____

_____

_____

_____

*A rock pile ceases to be a rock pile the moment a single man contemplates it, bearing within him the image of a cathedral.*

— Antoine de Saint-Exupery

## Building a legacy

How has your life experience as an adult changed the meaning of success for you? What did it used to be, and what is it now? How have you helped inspire and prepare others – friends, siblings, children, grandchildren – to achieve success on these terms?

_____

_____

_____

_____

_____

_____

_____

_____

_____

_____

Is there any one place in particular that you think is changed for the better due to your work there? How do you think you've made it a more rewarding, fair, friendly, interesting, or worthwhile place? Describe.

_____

_____

_____

_____

_____

_____

_____

_____

_____

Over the years, what special efforts have you made to provide your significant other, children, grandchildren, and other relatives and friends a welcoming place to stay or spend holidays? Did you often have dinners or get-togethers at your home, or invite houseguests to stay? How do you think your homemaking efforts have enriched your family life, your friend's lives, and your own life?

_____

_____

_____

_____

_____

_____

_____

_____

_____

What art or other objects in your home have brought you the most inspiration and delight over the years? Where do these objects come from? Did you or someone you know make any of these? Who would you like to have these objects eventually, and why?

_____

_____

_____

_____

_____

_____

_____

_____

_____

*A man is a success if he gets up in the morning and gets to bed at night, and in between he does what he wants to do.*

— Bob Dylan

## Bonding experiences

Can you think of a transition in your adult life that brought you closer to a relative or friend you weren't as close with before? Was it moving to a new town, becoming a grandparent, taking up the banjo? Who was the friend or relative? Can you remember a bonding moment you two shared?

_____

_____

_____

_____

_____

_____

_____

_____

_____

If you have a life partner, what life experiences have the two of you been through together that ultimately strengthened your commitment to one another? How did this experience clarify your priorities and devotion to each other?

_____

_____

_____

_____

_____

_____

_____

_____

_____

Can you think of a time you hit it off with someone, and instead of letting the connection drop there, took the initiative to strike up a friendship? Describe. How did you first meet, and what efforts did you make to get to know this person better? How did the friendship grow? Can you think of someone who actively pursued you as a friend? Describe.

_____

_____

_____

_____

_____

_____

_____

_____

_____

_____

_____

Can you think of a time as an adult when you asked a friend for help or support, and that friend came through for you with flying colors? Who? What were the circumstances? How were you rewarded with kindness or a closer bond for your bravery in letting your vulnerability show?

_____

_____

_____

_____

_____

_____

_____

_____

_____

_____

*We are each other's harvest;*
*we are each other's business;*
*we are each other's magnitude and bond.*

*— attributed to Gwendolyn Brooks*

## Focus on: Heroic feats of friendship

Certain friends are right there with you as you pass milestone after milestone in life – and when you consider the lengths they've gone to for you over the years, their stamina and strength may seem downright superhuman. Just think of the three friends you've been close to for the longest period of time and list them below, along with where and when you met. Next to each name, list all the life transitions when this friend has been there for you. Is there someone who has seen you through four major love interests, two graduate schools, one marriage, seven jobs, two kids, and three moves? Then, briefly describe the role this heroic friend played in each of these life events. Did you turn to this friend for input, laughter, support, gossip, advice, argument, reassurance, a place to stay or a point of departure? Describe.

Friend/Personal hero: _____

Where and when did you meet? _____

_____

Milestone Heroic feats _____

_____

Friend/Personal hero: _____

Where and when did you meet? _____

_____

Milestone Heroic feats _____

_____

Friend/Personal hero: _____

Where and when did you meet? _____

_____

Milestone Heroic feats _____

_____

If you're so motivated when you finish these tables, send out a card to each of these friends thanking them for their heroic acts of friendship over the years. If your friend is no longer alive, you might send the note to a surviving relative of this friend who'd appreciate it. Then jot down a few words about how it felt to write that card. If you get a response, include a few words about how it was received.

## Retirement and repose

If you haven't yet retired, when and where do you plan to retire? How would you like to spend your days?

_____

_____

_____

_____

_____

_____

_____

_____

_____

_____

If you're retired, when did you decide to retire, and what made you decide to retire at that point in your career? How did you celebrate your retirement, and who was there to mark the occasion with you? Can you recall any of the comments your colleagues made about working with you, and what you'd accomplished in your career?

_____

_____

_____

_____

_____

_____

_____

_____

_____

Where did you go after you retired, and what did you do there? Is this what you'd always wanted to do for your retirement, or was there a change in plan? Explain.

_____

_____

_____

_____

_____

_____

_____

_____

_____

_____

Was it difficult for you to adjust to having so much more time on your hands after you retired and/or your kids left home? Why or why not? What rewarding activities have you taken on that you weren't able to before – teaching at a community college, taking a ceramics class, spending quality time with your grandkids after school, writing this book?

_____

_____

_____

_____

_____

_____

_____

_____

_____

*Half our life is spent trying to find something to do with the time we have rushed through life trying to save.*

— Will Rogers

**Terms of endearment**

If you sustained a relationship for many years by this point, what do you think kept your relationship going for so long? What was the most trying time in your relationship, and how did you get past it? What is it about the person your loved one has become over the years that delights and amazes you?

_____

_____

_____

_____

_____

_____

_____

_____

_____

_____

What are all the pet names you've called one another over the years? What are the origins of these nicknames?  Which ones are your favorites, and why?

_____

_____

_____

_____

_____

_____

_____

_____

_____

_____

What habits do you think you picked up from your loved one over the years? Would you consider this a good thing, or a bad thing? What signature expressions or sayings have you adopted as your own? What about vice versa?

_____
_____
_____
_____
_____
_____
_____
_____
_____
_____

Can you recall any particularly special anniversary celebration, Valentine's Day, or other romantic occasion? Perhaps when your friends threw you that surprise party, when your family pooled their resources to send you on a second honeymoon, or maybe when your longtime love managed to cook up a candlelight dinner without any incidents requiring the intervention of the local fire department?

_____
_____
_____
_____
_____
_____
_____
_____
_____

*Sexiness wears thin after a while, and beauty fades, but to be married to a man who makes you laugh everyday — ah, now that's a real treat!*

— *Joanne Woodward, in reference to husband Paul Newman*

## Instant memories: Display of affection

If you have a significant other, the memorabilia of your years together that you proudly display on the mantelpiece, bedside table, and refrigerator door are just a small fraction of the photos, cards, and other romantic reminders you keep stockpiled in desk drawers and shoe boxes in the closet. What good are they doing anyone there?! Take an inventory of all this ephemera, and see if you can find at least one or two meaningful items from each year you've been together. Do you have the note you sent with flowers on her first day of work as a doctor? Or the aloha shirt you bought for his first day of retirement? Can you dig up the ticket stubs from that Hungarian movie festival you went to on your last anniversary, not realizing there were no subtitles? List some of these items below, the year in your life together that they represent, and what meaning they hold for you.

Year ____ in our relationship: Date _____.

Describe this item. _____

_____

What does this item represent to you?

_____

Year ____ in our relationship: Date _____.

Describe this item. _____

_____

What does this item represent to you? _____

_____

Year ____ in our relationship: Date _____.

Describe this item. _____

_____

What does this item represent to you? _____

_____

Year ___ in our relationship: Date _____.

Describe this item. _____

_____

What does this item represent to you? _____

_____

Year ___ in our relationship: Date _____.

Describe this item. _____

_____

What does this item represent to you? _____

_____

Year ___ in our relationship: Date _____.

Describe this item. _____

_____

What does this item represent to you? _____

_____

Year ___ in our relationship: Date _____.

Describe this item. _____

_____

What does this item represent to you? _____

_____

Year ___ in our relationship: Date _____.

Describe this item. _____

_____

What does this item represent to you? _____

_____

Year ___ in our relationship: Date _____.

Describe this item. _____

_____

What does this item represent to you? _____

_____

Year ___ in our relationship: Date _____.

Describe this item. _____

_____

What does this item represent to you? _____

_____

Year ___ in our relationship: Date _____.

Describe this item. _____

_____

What does this item represent to you? _____

_____

Year ___ in our relationship: Date _____.

Describe this item. _____

_____

What does this item represent to you? _____

_____

Year ___ in our relationship: Date _____.

Describe this item. _____

_____

What does this item represent to you? _____

_____

Add additional entries as needed; try to identify one item for each of your years together and write a few words on what it symbolizes about your relationship. Then fold an index card in half so that it stands up like a tent, and copy your notes about each item on the front. Next, clear off a mantelpiece, table, or shelf so that you can display each item alongside the appropriate tent card. Add flowers and a candle or two, and you'll have a romantic display of affection that should impress your loved one far more than that off-key singing telegram from last year's anniversary…

## Family ties

How have your relationships to your closest relatives grown or evolved over the years? Which of your family relationships has changed the most significantly in your adult life? Is it the one you have with a parent, sibling, aunt, uncle, cousin? How would you describe that relationship as it was years ago, and as it stands today?

_____

_____

_____

_____

_____

_____

_____

_____

_____

_____

If you had children or stepchildren, how would you say your relationship to them evolved as they grew into adults? Do you think of any of them as friends? Why or why not? If you were to boast a little about the individuals they've become as adults, what would you say about them?

_____

_____

_____

_____

_____

_____

_____

_____

Did you have or adopt any children later in life, or become a stepparent? How did the arrival of each child enrich your family life, and your own life? Describe.

_____

_____

_____

_____

_____

_____

Is there anyone you feel has become an honorary family member of yours over the years? Who? How did you meet, and how did this person become such an integral part of your family?

_____

_____

_____

_____

_____

_____

Were you ever a godparent or honorary aunt or uncle to a friend's child? What are the personal rewards and challenges that came with this role? Can you tell your favorite story about this child? What about a story about the adult this child has since become?

_____

_____

_____

_____

_____

_____

*It kills you to see them grow up.*
*But I guess it would kill you*
*quicker if they didn't.*

— Barbara Kingsolver

## Grandkids

Do you have any grandchildren? If so, list their names, parents and birth dates below.

_____

_____

_____

_____

_____

_____

_____

_____

_____

_____

What five words come to mind to describe each grandchild?

_____

_____

_____

_____

_____

_____

_____

_____

_____

_____

_____

_____

Can you think of one memory you have of each of your grandchildren that reveals something about their characters? Describe.

_____

_____

_____

_____

_____

_____

_____

_____

_____

_____

What role have you played in each of their lives, and how often do you usually see each of them? What do they call you, and what are your pet names for them? Describe.

_____

_____

_____

_____

_____

_____

_____

_____

_____

_____

## Leader of the pack

Were you ever a trailblazer in your family? Were you the first woman in your family to get a college degree, the first member of your immediate family who didn't go in the family business, the first person in your extended family to marry outside your religion? How has this broken down barriers for others in your family?

_____

_____

_____

_____

_____

_____

_____

_____

_____

Can you recall a time when you played a pivotal role in your family – helping to mediate a family conflict, hosting a family holiday with the entire extended family, teaching the kids about a cultural tradition your ancestors practiced? Describe.

_____

_____

_____

_____

_____

_____

_____

_____

_____

_____

Have you ever helped others get a boost in their career – by recommending a former employee for a great job, helping a friend complete a graduate school application, or mentoring a less experienced co-worker? Describe. What did this person go on to do?

_____

_____

_____

_____

_____

_____

_____

_____

Have you ever come to another person's rescue in a crisis? This could mean performing CPR or diving into the water to save someone, but don't forget about other less obviously heroic acts: opening your home to a cousin going through a divorce, going with a friend to get the results of a biopsy, preparing liquid lunches for your sister after all her wisdom teeth were removed. How did this person show appreciation towards you?

_____

_____

_____

_____

_____

_____

_____

_____

## Making history: For the greater good

Newspaper headlines often focus on the crisis of the hour – but if you take a longer view at what's happened in the world over the course of your adult life, you'll find some promising developments too. Consider what has happened in your day in the following areas:

**Politics:** Were any wars ended or prevented? Any laws passed or court cases decided that you consider landmark decisions? Any leaders show vision or integrity, do you think?

**Science and technology:** Any new cures or treatments for debilitating diseases? What about devices that save people considerable time and expense, or create less pollution?

**Arts:** Were any artworks created that you consider masterpieces? Did any spectacular shows or plays premiere? What about great music, book or film releases?

**Business:** Any promising new business models developed, improvements made in workplace conditions, or worthwhile philanthropic ventures pursued?

_____

_____

_____

_____

_____

_____

_____

_____

_____

_____

_____

_____

_____

_____

_____

_____

_____

_____

## Making history: For the greater good, cont.

Now consider how your actions have been in synch with the promising developments you've witnessed in your lifetime.

**Politics:** Did you rally behind or protest any particular law or political candidate?

**Science and technology:** Have you donated or raised funds to support research on a particular disease, or helped to develop time-saving technologies in your own work?

**Arts:** Did you volunteer or contribute funds to an arts organization, urge others to see a particular show or film, or recommend an album or book you thought was outstanding?

**Business:** Did you apply any promising business practices, push for more flexible work schedules or improved health and safety provisions, or participate in a corporate giving campaign at your company?

_____

_____

_____

_____

_____

_____

_____

_____

_____

_____

_____

_____

_____

_____

_____

_____

_____

_____

_____

_____

*The ultimate measure of a man is not where he stands in moments of comfort, but where he stands at times of challenge and controversy.*

— Martin Luther King, Jr.

# CHAPTER NINE

# Looking forward: Prime of life

*All may have, if they dare try, a glorious life.*

*— George Herbert*

## True character

What would you say are your best qualities, and what circumstances bring them out?

_____

_____

_____

_____

_____

_____

_____

_____

_____

_____

_____

What is your definition of leadership? Can you think of a time when you lived up to this definition of leadership? Describe.

_____

_____

_____

_____

_____

_____

_____

_____

_____

_____

_____

Do you know what you would say are the biggest mistakes you've made in your life, and what do you think you've learned from making them?

_____

_____

_____

_____

_____

_____

_____

_____

_____

_____

Can you think of a personal motto or value you've made a conscious effort to live by, even when it's been inconvenient or difficult? "There's great virtue in small kindnesses," "Always save for a rainy day," "Never lose the language and culture of your ancestors"? What has been your greatest test in living up to this value?

_____

_____

_____

_____

_____

_____

_____

_____

_____

*The battles that count aren't the ones for gold medals. The struggles within yourself — the invisible, inevitable battles inside all of us — that's where it's at.*

— Jesse Owens

## Realizations

Have you ever regretted your decision to leave a relationship, or stay in a relationship as long as you did? Explain. Has this regret helped prevent you from making the same mistake twice? Explain.

_____

_____

_____

_____

_____

_____

_____

_____

_____

_____

When was the first time as an adult that you learned the power of the word "no"? Who did you say it to, and why? Was it to a child asking you for an expensive toy, a boss telling you to fetch coffee, a friend asking for a large loan? Was it easier to say no to people after that?

_____

_____

_____

_____

_____

_____

_____

_____

_____

_____

Did you ever come to the realization that you should have heeded a friend's or relative's advice – about taking a boring job, associating with a slightly unstable friend, loaning your car to your lovable but somewhat reckless nephew? Explain.

_____

_____

_____

_____

_____

_____

_____

_____

_____

_____

Ever realize that your personal priorities had gotten out of whack? Were you neglecting your family, forgetting to look after your health, or allowing your creative pursuits to fall by the wayside? Did you come to this realization on your own, or did a courageous person point it out to you? Explain.

_____

_____

_____

_____

_____

_____

_____

_____

_____

_____

*If there is a sin against life,*
*it consists perhaps not so much in*
*despairing of life as in hoping for*
*another life and in eluding the*
*implacable grandeur of this life.*

*— Albert Camus*

**Live and learn**

What new technologies have you adopted in the course of your lifetime? What can you remember about the first time you came into contact with or made use of this technology?

_____

_____

_____

_____

_____

_____

_____

_____

_____

_____

What values or lessons have you learned from young people in your life – younger co-workers, neighbors, children, grandchildren? Explain.

_____

_____

_____

_____

_____

_____

_____

_____

_____

_____

_____

Which of your political or religious beliefs do your siblings, significant other, children or grandchildren not seem to subscribe to as you do? Why do you think this is the case? Has this created any tension between you? Have they shifted your position at all? Why or why not?

_____

_____

_____

_____

_____

_____

_____

_____

_____

How has your approach to family life changed with the times – are you more accepting of religious or cultural differences among family members, do you embrace stepchildren as beloved family members, is being the decision-maker less important to you than it used to be? Describe.

_____

_____

_____

_____

_____

_____

_____

_____

_____

## Elder statesman

Which of your religious beliefs have been the greatest comfort to you? Which have been the greatest challenge? Why?

_____

_____

_____

_____

_____

_____

_____

_____

_____

_____

What advice would you offer about aging? In what ways is growing older generally underrated? Overrated?

_____

_____

_____

_____

_____

_____

_____

_____

_____

If there's one common misperception you'd most like to correct about people of your ethnic or cultural heritage, what would it be? What would you like people to know about your ethnic or cultural heritage that isn't widely known?

_____

_____

_____

_____

_____

_____

_____

_____

_____

_____

What social problem would you like to dedicate yourself to learning more about and trying to solve?

_____

_____

_____

_____

_____

_____

_____

_____

_____

_____

_____

## Making history: Circles of influence

Times have changed – and if you have anything to say about it, they're not done changing yet. In your lifetime, how have you personally seen things get things better and worse in the following areas:

**Family:** _____

Better: _____

Worse: _____

**Workplace:** _____

Better: _____

Worse: _____

**Neighborhood:** _____

Better: _____

Worse: _____

**Nation:** _____

Better: _____

Worse: _____

**World:** _____

Better: _____

Worse: _____

## Making history: Circles of influence, cont.

Now take a critical look at the problematic situations described above. What one action could you take that might improve each predicament, and provide a positive example for others to follow?

Family: _____

_____

_____

Workplace: _____

_____

_____

Neighborhood: _____

_____

_____

Nation: _____

_____

_____

World: _____

_____

_____

**Life cycles**

Is there a person you've lost who you are still reminded of often? Who is this person? What are some of the sights, sounds, and occasions that bring this person to mind?

_____

_____

_____

_____

_____

_____

_____

_____

_____

_____

Is there someone you lost years ago who you feel you are still learning from? Who? How has this person's example helped to guide you?

_____

_____

_____

_____

_____

_____

_____

_____

_____

_____

Can you think of anyone who entered your life only recently who has become important to you? Who is this person? How did you meet?

_____

_____

_____

_____

_____

_____

_____

_____

_____

_____

_____

_____

_____

_____

_____

_____

_____

_____

_____

_____

_____

_____

_____

_____

_____

_____

*Old friends pass away, new friends appear. It is just like the days. An old day passes, a new day arrives. The important thing is to make it meaningful: a meaningful friend — or a meaningful day.*

— attributed to Tenzin Gyatso, 14th Dalai Lama

## Declarations of independence

If you could free yourself from any one obligation tomorrow, what would it be? Why?
Could you actually do this? Why or why not?

_____

_____

_____

_____

_____

_____

_____

_____

_____

Can you think of a strong opinion, belief or political position you've held onto for a long
time, but you're actually not so sure about anymore? Would you like to go on the record
now and retract or revise this opinion?

_____

_____

_____

_____

_____

_____

_____

_____

_____

_____

What would you like to be doing more of and less of a year from now? Who would you like to see more of and less of a year from now? What's stopping you from putting these changes in motion now?

_____

_____

_____

_____

_____

_____

_____

_____

_____

_____

What secret, anxiety, or guilt plagues you that would you like to let go of right now, and be done with trying to stifle? Write it below.

_____

_____

_____

_____

_____

_____

_____

_____

_____

_____

*Truth is always exciting. Speak it, then.*
*Life is dull without it.*

— *Pearl Buck*

## Sweet mysteries of life

What would you say are the most diabolical deeds and miraculous feats you've witnessed in the course of your lifetime?

_____

_____

_____

_____

_____

_____

_____

_____

_____

_____

What would you say has been your greatest curse in life? What about your greatest blessing?

_____

_____

_____

_____

_____

_____

_____

_____

_____

_____

_____

What do you hope the afterlife is like? How do you picture it?

_____

_____

_____

_____

_____

_____

_____

_____

_____

_____

What one question would you most like to have answered?

_____

_____

_____

_____

_____

_____

_____

_____

_____

_____

_____

*All truths are easy to understand once they are discovered; the point is to discover them.*

— Galileo Galilei

## Following your bliss

What activities give you the strongest sense of purpose nowadays: volunteering with a food program, being active in your community or place of worship? Describe. How is this activity challenging for you, and what makes it so rewarding?

_____

_____

_____

_____

_____

_____

_____

_____

_____

_____

What travel destinations currently top of your list of places you'd like to visit? What is it that attracts you about this place – great snorkeling, interesting sights, friends who live nearby? Do you have any plans to visit any of these in the near future? Describe.

_____

_____

_____

_____

_____

_____

_____

_____

_____

_____

What daily rituals do you find most satisfying lately – doing the entire crossword puzzle by yourself, having tea with your significant other in the afternoon, preparing dinner? What is it you like best about this ritual?

_____

_____

_____

_____

_____

_____

_____

_____

_____

_____

What subject are you determined to learn more about: documentary film, Indonesian history, online auctions? What piqued your interest in this particular subject? What have you learned thus far, and what's your plan of action for delving deeper into the subject?

_____

_____

_____

_____

_____

_____

_____

_____

_____

_____

## Focus on: Creativity

If you don't think of yourself as a creative person, just look around your home and the homes of your loved ones at all the things you've made, built or designed over the years: bookshelves, clothes, coffee tables, necklaces, fishing lures, garden boxes, greeting cards, vases, sculptures, holiday ornaments, web sites, duck decoys, pillows, bathroom tiles, maybe even the house itself. If this doesn't convince you of your creative capacity, dig out some school transcripts and report cards, and let these remind you of all the creative endeavors you've undertaken in the course of your educational career. Remember that doghouse you built in woodshop in high school, or that etching you made in your college printmaking class? Include these on your list of all your past creative ventures below, along with a few words about what inspired you to pursue it and what you got out of the experience. Then identify at least one project you'd make today if you were to pursue this creative field.

Creative venture: _____

What inspired this venture? _____

What did you get out of the experience? _____

What would you make today using this creative skill? _____


Creative venture: _____

What inspired this venture? _____

What did you get out of the experience? _____

What would you make today using this creative skill? _____


Creative venture: _____

What inspired this venture? _____

What did you get out of the experience? _____

What would you make today using this creative skill? _____


Creative venture: _____

What inspired this venture? _____

What did you get out of the experience? _____

What would you make today using this creative skill? _____

Creative venture: _____

What inspired this venture? _____

What did you get out of the experience? _____

What would you make today using this creative skill? _____


Creative venture: _____

What inspired this venture? _____

What did you get out of the experience? _____

What would you make today using this creative skill? _____


Creative venture: _____

What inspired this venture? _____

What did you get out of the experience? _____

What would you make today using this creative skill? _____


Creative venture: _____

What inspired this venture? _____

What did you get out of the experience? _____

What would you make today using this creative skill? _____


Creative venture: _____

What inspired this venture? _____

What did you get out of the experience? _____

What would you make today using this creative skill? _____


Creative venture: _____

What inspired this venture? _____

What did you get out of the experience? _____

What would you make today using this creative skill? _____

Now that you can see how creatively inclined you really are, is there anything you'd like to create that you've never attempted before? A gingerbread house, a robot, a taxidermy fish, an ikebana flower arrangement – or perhaps some inconceivable combination of all the above? List these creative interests below, along with a few words about what interests you in this field. Then, call around to your local arts organizations and colleges and find out if you can find a match for any of the creative interests listed below and above. Be sure to explain what kinds of projects you have in mind, so they can hook you up with the most appropriate class or workshop for your interests.

Creative venture: _____

What interests you in this creative pursuit?_____

_____

_____

Creative venture: _____

What interests you in this creative pursuit?_____

_____

_____

Creative venture: _____

What interests you in this creative pursuit?_____

_____

_____

Creative venture: _____

What interests you in this creative pursuit?_____

_____

_____

Creative venture: _____

What interests you in this creative pursuit?_____

_____

_____

*The secret to staying young is to live honestly, eat slowly, and lie about your age.*

*— Lucille Ball*

## Vision for the future

If you had to identify three specific changes taking place in the world right now that you think are especially promising indicators for the future, what would those be?

_____

_____

_____

_____

_____

_____

_____

_____

_____

What three changes do you see occurring in the world today that you think need to be reversed?

_____

_____

_____

_____

_____

_____

_____

_____

_____

_____

Imagine what daily life will be like 10 years from now. How do you think it will be different than how it is today? How do you think it will be similar?

_____

_____

_____

_____

_____

_____

_____

Imagine what daily life will be like 25 years from now. How do you think it will be different than how it is today? How do you think it will be similar?

_____

_____

_____

_____

_____

_____

_____

Imagine what daily life will be like 100 years from now. How do you think it will be different than how it is today? How do you think it will be similar?

_____

_____

_____

_____

_____

_____

_____

## A charmed existence

What three changes would you most like to see happen in the world during your lifetime – a cure for cancer, more national funding for the arts, a significant drop in the violent crime rate in your hometown? What can you do to help make sure these hopes are realized?

_____

_____

_____

_____

_____

_____

_____

_____

_____

If you have siblings, what are your three highest hopes for each of them? What can you do to help make sure these hopes are realized?

_____

_____

_____

_____

_____

_____

_____

_____

_____

_____

If you have children, what are your three highest hopes for each of them? What can you do to help make sure these hopes are realized?

_____

_____

_____

_____

_____

_____

_____

_____

_____

_____

If you have grandchildren, what are your three highest hopes for each of them? What can you do to help make sure these hopes are realized?

_____

_____

_____

_____

_____

_____

_____

_____

_____

_____

If you have a significant other, what dreams do you hope may yet come true for your loved one in the years to come? What can you do to help make this happen?

_____

_____

_____

_____

_____

_____

_____

_____

_____

_____

What dreams of your own do you hope to realize in your years ahead? What can you do to help make this happen?

_____

_____

_____

_____

_____

_____

_____

_____

_____

_____

_____

*It is never too late to be what*
*you might have been.*

— George Eliot

## Instant memories: Share your story

Kick your feet up, make yourself comfortable, and prepare to read a fascinating book: *My Life: A Collection of Memories,* as written by you. As you turn these pages, notice what sections make you laugh, cry, think, or all three. What are some of the recurring themes in these powerful passages? Are the stories that resonate the deepest the ones you tell about your significant other, or cultural heritage, or a devastating loss? What does this tell you about the meaning of the life you've led thus far, and the meaning of the life you have yet to live? Share your thoughts below.

_____

_____

_____

_____

_____

_____

_____

_____

_____

_____

_____

_____

_____

_____

_____

_____

_____

_____

_____

_____

_____

Now that you've come to the end of this book, you'll notice that you're not the only one with a starring role in it. Friends and family have made your life story a rollicking adventure, and a tale well worth telling. So share this book with them if you haven't already, because your story is their story too.

_____

_____

_____

_____

_____

_____

_____

_____

_____

_____

_____

_____

_____

_____

_____

_____

_____

_____

_____

_____

_____

_____

*It is good to have an end to journey towards, but it is the journey that matters in the end.*

— Ursula K. Le Guin

_____

_____

_____

_____

_____

_____

_____

_____

_____

_____

_____

_____

_____

_____

_____

_____

_____

_____

_____

_____

_____

_____

_____

_____

_____

_____